ighth Symposium on
ucleic Acids Chemistry

ld in Sapporo, Japan
ugust 21st ~ 23rd, 1980

LEIC ACIDS SYMPOSIUM SERIES No.8

iled by Angela E. Pritchard

L an Information Retrieval publication

Eighth Symposium on Nucleic Acids Chemistry

held in Sapporo, Japan
August 21st – 23rd, 1980

NUCLEIC ACIDS SYMPOSIUM SERIES No.8

Compiled by Angela E. Pritchard

ISSN 035-1048

Contents

Contents continued overleaf

Author index

Syntheses of sulfur-containing nucleoside analogs

Haruo Ogura, Hiroshi Takahashi and Osamu Sato

School of Pharmaceutical Sciences, Kitasato University, Shirokane, Minato-ku, Tokyo 108, Japan

ABSTRACT

Reaction of glycosyl isothiocyanates (1a,b,c) with diazo compounds or chloroethylamine gave glycosylamino-1,2,3-thiadiazoles and glycosylimidazolidine-2-thiones. Similar reaction of 1a,b with ethanolamine afforded N-glycosyl-N'-hydroxyethylthioureides, followed by treatment of thionyl chloride to give glycosyliminothiazolidines. N-Glycosyl-N'-amidinothiocarboxamides were treated with thionyl chloride to give glycosyl s-triazin $\underline{S}$-oxides. N-Glycosyl-N'-(6-amino-1,3-dimethyl-2,4-dioxopyrimidin-5-yl)thioureides were oxidized with NBS into pyrimidotriazine glycosides.

INTRODUCTION

In previous papers, we reported the synthesis of nucleoside analogs from the reaction of glycosyl isothiocyanates (1a, b,c) with carbon-[1] and nitrogen-[2]nucleophiles. We describe here a facile synthesis of nucleoside analogs through a reaction of 1a,b,c with nucleophiles such as diazo compounds, diamines or amidines.

RESULTS

Reaction of glycosyl isothiocyanates (1a,b,c) with diazomethane under cooling gave corresponding glycosylamino-1,2,3-thiadiazoles (2a,b,c) in a good yield. Treatment of 1a,b,c with diazoacetate in dioxane with heating afforded 2a,b,c in 26-30% yields. Reaction of 1a,b,c with chloroethylamine (n=2) or chloropropylamine (n=3) was easily proceeded and the corresponding cyclized product (4a,b,c) was obtained in a fair yield. 1a,b was treated with ethanolamine in benzene under refluxing to yield the thioureides (6a,b), followed by treatment of thionyl chloride under cooling to afford 7a,b in 87-94% yield. Reaction of 1a,b,c with amidines under basic conditions gave corresponding glycosyl isothiobiurets (8: R'= OMe, SMe, NH_2) or N-glycosyl-N'-amidinothiocarboxamides (9: R'= H, Me) in a fair yield. The compound (8) was treated with triethyl orthoformate under heating to afford s-triazine glycoside (10) in 90-95% yield[3]. When the amidinothiocarboxamide was similarly treated with triethyl orthoformate, a one-carbon inserted product was not obtained and the starting material was recovered. Treatment of 9 with thionyl chloride-pyridine under cooling gave the respective glycosyl s-triazine S-oxide (11) in a good yield. The ring constraction of triazine S-oxide into triazole glycosides[4] was unsuccessful. 1a,b,c was treated with 5,6-diamino-1,3-dimethyluracil or o-phenylenediamine in acetonitrile or benzene under refluxing to give thioureido compounds (13)[5]. NBS (N-bromosuccinimide) oxidation[4,6] of 13 gave the cyclized products (14a,b).

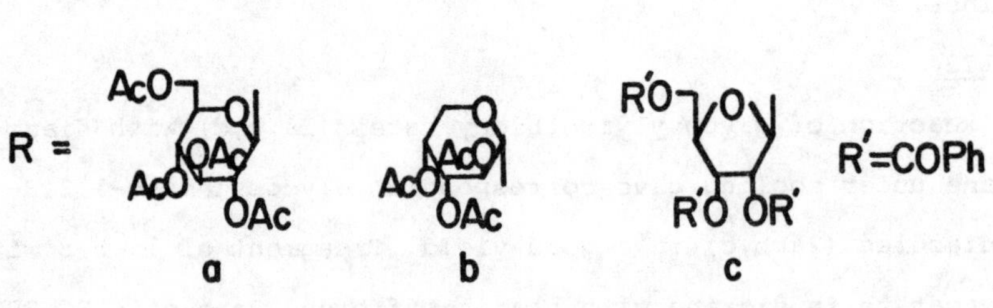

R =

a   b   c

R'=COPh

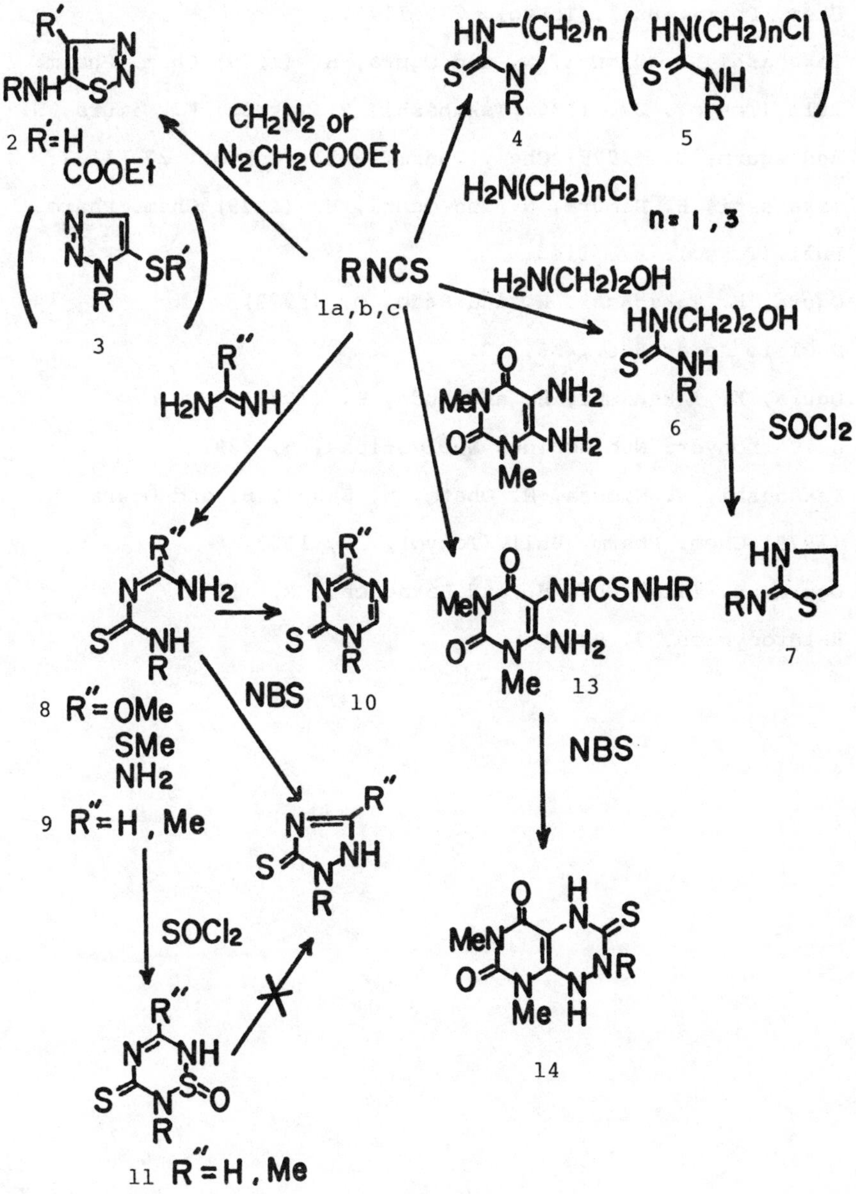

RNCS
1a,b,c
CH_2N_2 or
N_2CH_2COOEt
2 R′=H
COOEt
3
4
5
$H_2N(CH_2)nCl$
n= 1,3
$H_2N(CH_2)_2OH$
6
$SOCl_2$
7
13
NBS
14
8 R″= OMe
SMe
NH_2
9 R″=H, Me
10
NBS
$SOCl_2$
11 R″=H, Me

REFERENCES

1 Takahashi, H. Nimura, N. and Ogura, H. (1979)

  Chem. Pharm. Bull.(Tokyo). 27, 1147.

2 Takahashi, H. Nimura, N. and Ogura, H. (1979) Chem. Pharm.

  Bull.(Tokyo). 27, 1130. Takahashi, H. Takeda, K. Nimura, N.

  and Ogura, H. (1979) Chem. Pharm. Bull.(Tokyo). 27, 1137.

  Takahashi, H. Nimura, N. and Ogura, H. (1979) Chem. Pharm.

  Bull.(Tokyo). 27, 1143.

3 Ogura, H. Takahashi, H. and Sato, O. (1979)

  Nucleic Acids Res., S6, 13.

4 Ogura, H. Takahashi, H. and Kudo, E. (1978)

  J. Carbohydr. Nucleosides Nucleotides, 5, 329.

5 Takahashi, H. Nimura, N. Obata, N. Sakai, H. and Ogura, H.

  (1979) Chem. Pharm. Bull.(Tokyo). 27, 1153.

6 Ogura, H. Takahashi, H. and Sakaguchi, M. (1975)

  Heterocycles, 3, 93.

Dibutyltin oxide – phenyl isocyanate system for regioselective phenylcarbamoylation of the hydroxy-groups of ribonucleosides

Yoshiharu Ishido, Ichiro Hirao, Kiyotaka Itoh, Kazuaki Tamaki and Younosuke Araki

Department of Chemistry, Faculty of Science, Tokyo Institute of Technology, O-okayama, Meguro-ku, Tokyo 152, Japan

ABSTRACT

For partial phenylcarbamoylation of the hydroxy-groups of ribonucleosides, dibutyltin oxide – phenyl isocyanate system was found to be surperior to the bis(tributyltin) oxide – phenyl isocyanate system from the standpoint of reaction procedures including isolation of the products; the reaction was proved to occur with similar regioselectivity and to give the corresponding 5'-, 3'-, and 2'-O-phenylcarbamoyl derivatives in good yields, respectively, due to the conditions used.

INTRODUCTION

Carbamoylation reaction of alcohols through organotin compounds and isocyanates[1] has been successfully extended to regioselective phenylcarbamoylation of the hydroxy-groups of ribonucleosides[2], in which two kinds of procedures were found to give differently protected ribonucleosides, i.e., 1) Procedure A involves the formation of the corresponding alkoxides by treating a ribonucleoside with 0.5 mol. equiv. of bis(tributyltin) oxide in toluene, followed by the addition reaction to an equimolar phenyl isocyanate; it gave the corresponding 5'-phenylcarbamate predominantly. 2) Procedure B involves no alkoxide formation procedure, but a one-stage treatment of a ribonucleoside with phenyl isocyanate (1.8 ∿ 1.5 mol. equiv.) in the presence of bis-(tributyltin) oxide (0.5 ∿ 0.16 mol. equiv.); it gave the corresponding 3'-phenylcarbamate regioselectively. However, bis(tributyltin) oxide is not so convenient because it is a liquid, and caused some difficulty in separation of the resulting ribonucleoside derivatives and tin species. Accordingly, we subsequently attempted to use dibutyltin oxide for the phenylcarbamoylation reaction, taking into consideration its greater suitability since it is a solid.

RESULTS AND DISCUSSION

A treatment of $\underline{N}^6$-benzyladenosine (1) with dibutyltin oxide (catalytic amount) — phenyl isocyanate (1 mol. equiv.) in toluene (Procedure B) gave $\underline{N}^6$-benzyl-3'-$\underline{O}$-phenylcarbamoyladenosine (2) in 81%[3] yield. The regioselectivity observed here is similar to that in the reaction involving bis(tributyltin) oxide in place of dibutyltin oxide[2], but the present reaction was smoothly induced even at room temperature. This was different from the reaction discussed previously[2], in which it was necessary to lower the reaction

temperature below 0°C in order to facilitate phenylcarbamoylation. The dibutyltin oxide which remained in the system as a suspension was easily removed by filtration with TOYO-131 filter paper after the reaction. In the present reaction, dibutyltin oxide was postulated to behave as an adduct with phenyl isocyanate; this adduct is soluble in the solvent used and catalytically induces the reaction on the hydroxy-group of (1) by the remaining phenyl isocyanate. It seems to be invalid to explain the reaction by assuming the alkoxide intermediate as has been postulated in the reaction by Procedure A[2]. Some experimental evidence will be presented. Similar to Procedure B invovling bis(tributyltin) oxide, the regioselectivity in the formation of the 3'-$\underline{O}$-phenylcarbamoyl derivative was lowered on elevation of the polarity of the solvent system by the addition of $\underline{N},\underline{N}$-dimethylformamide etc. Triphenyltin acetate was also used in place of dibutyltin oxide in this reaction, and was found to give similar results.

Similar results obtained with other ribonucleoside derivatives and those through Procedure A will also be described.

REFERENCES AND FOOTNOTES

1 Davies, A. G. (1969) Synthesis, 1, 56 - 64; Bloodworth, A. J. and Davies, A. G. (1972) Chem. & Ind., 17, 490 - 494.
2 Ishido, Y., Hirao, I., Sakairi, N., and Araki, Y. (1979) Nucleic Acid Res., Spec. Publ., 6, s 37 - 40; idem. (1979) Heterocycles, 13, 181 - 185.
3 This was determined through high performance liquid chromatography with a Varian LC-8520 apparatus.

A new and facile synthesis of purine 2'-amino-2'-deoxyribosides by a combination of chemical and enzymatic reactions

Hirokazu Morisawa, Takashi Utagawa, Tsuyoshi Nakamatsu, Shigeru Yamanaka and Akihiro Yamazaki

Central Research Laboratories, Ajinomoto Co., Inc., 1-1 Suzuki-cho, Kawasaki-ku, Kawasaki 210, Japan

ABSTRACT

An enzymatic synthesis of 2'-amino-2'-deoxy-2-chloroinosine and its chemical conversion to purine 2'-amino-2'-deoxyribosides are described. In addition, some of 2'-amino-2'-deoxyribosides of 6-substituted purine were also prepared from 2'-amino-2'-deoxyinosine.

We have developed[1,2] a new and practical method for synthesizing biologically interesting purine arabinosides, such as Ara-A and Ara-G (Ara-X), by an enzymatic transarabinosylation between purine bases and ara-U (Scheme 1-a).

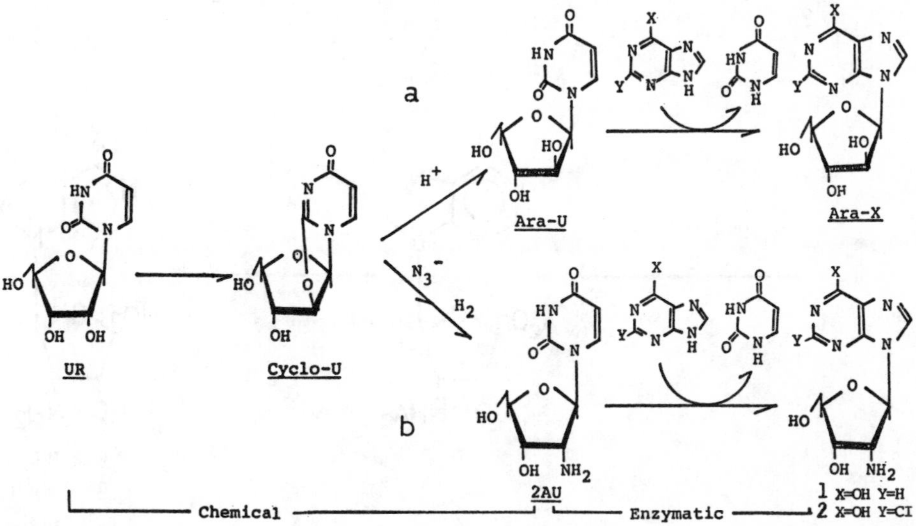

Scheme I

Recently 2'-amino-2'-deoxyribosides of guanine (3)[3] and adenine (8),[4,5] which had antitumor, antibacterial or anti-mycoplasmal activity, have been isolated as antibiotics in Japan. The finding stimulated our interest in synthesis of purine nucleosides having 2-aminoribose using an enzymatic transglyco-sylation method.

More recently we have shown[6] that 2'-amino-2'-deoxyinosine (1) can be easily obtained by an enzymatic transaminoribosyla-tion between hypoxanthine and 2'-amino-2'-deoxyuridine (2-AU) prepared from uridine (Scheme 1-b). We now wish to report that this procedure can be extended to the synthesis of 2'-amino-2'-deoxy-2-chloroinosine (2) which is convertible to some biologi-cally interesting derivatives. When a mixture of intact cells

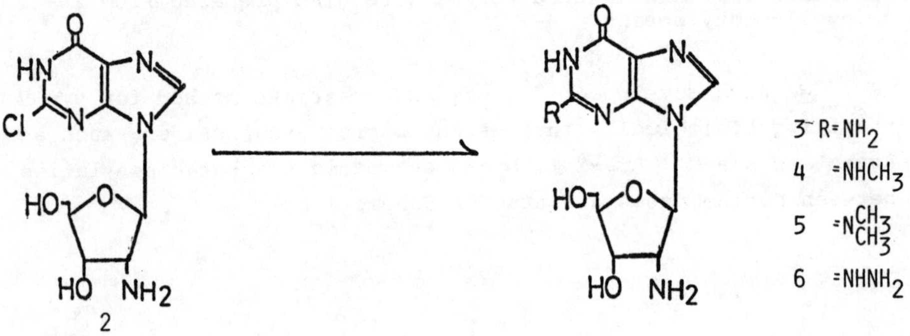

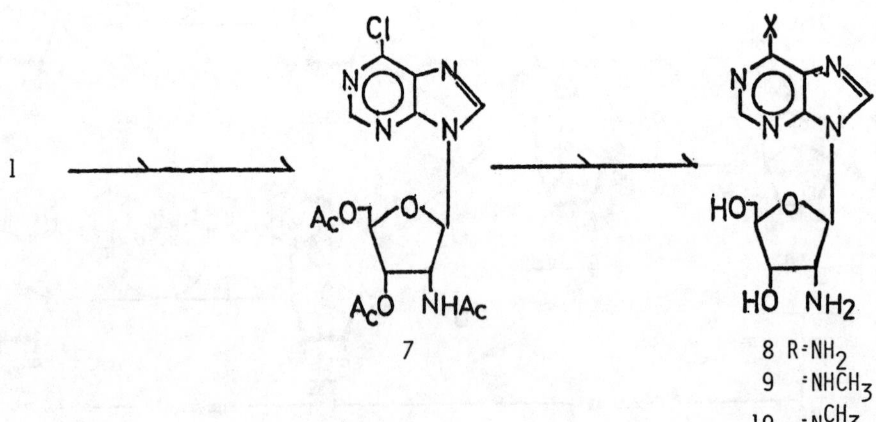

$$3 \quad R = NH_2$$
$$4 \quad = NHCH_3$$
$$5 \quad = N\begin{matrix}CH_3\\CH_3\end{matrix}$$
$$6 \quad = NHNH_2$$

$$8 \quad R = NH_2$$
$$9 \quad = NHCH_3$$
$$10 \quad = N\begin{matrix}CH_3\\CH_3\end{matrix}$$

Scheme 2

of <u>Erwinia herbicola</u> AJ 2803, 2-chlorohypoxanthine and 2-AU in
phosphate buffer (pH 7.0) was incubated at 60 °C for 20 hours,
compound 2 was formed easily (Scheme 1-b). This compound
should be very useful for the preparation of 2-substituted
derivatives of 1. Amination of 2 in methanolic ammonia afforded
compound 3 which had been synthesized by several methods.[7]
Treatment of 2 with methylamine, dimethylamine and hydrazine
gave easily N^2-substituted derivatives (4,5 and 6)of 3, respectively . Acetylation of 1 followed by chlorination gave 6-chloro
derivative (7) which, after N-deacetylation with methanolic
sodium methoxide, was transformed to the 2'-amino-2'-deoxyribo-
sides of adenine[7,8] and N^6-substituted adenine[9] (9 and 10)
(Scheme 2). In this case, N-deacetylation was incomplete,
giving the poor yield of the products.

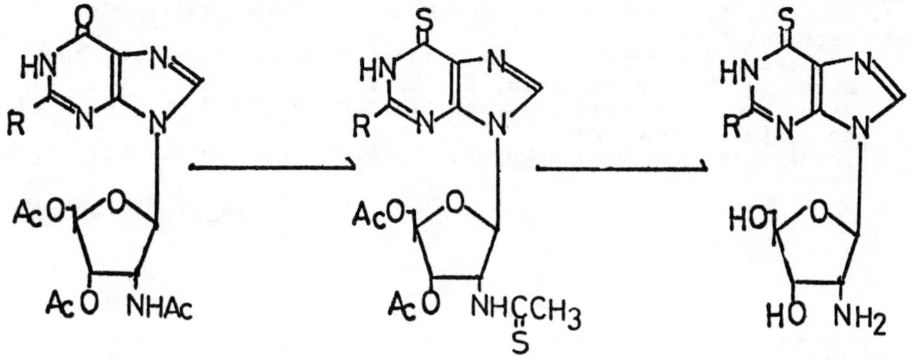

11 R=H
12 R=NHAc

13 R=H
14 R=NHCCH$_3$
   S

15 R=H
16 R=NH$_2$

Scheme 3

On the other hand, thiation of the fully acetylated
compounds (11 and 12) with phosphorus pentasulfide followed by
deblocking afforded 6-thio derivatives (15 and 16) in relatively
poor yields, respectively (Scheme 3).
The above combination method by enzymatic and chemical

reactions appears to provide an attractive route for the synthesis of 3 and 8 and their analogs, which have been difficult to obtain. Biological assay of the compounds prepared in this study is now under investigation.

REFERENCES
1. Utagawa, T., Morisawa, H., Miyoshi, T., Yoshinaga, F., Yamazaki, A. and Mitsugi, K. (1980) FEBS Lett., 109, 261.
2. Morisawa, H., Utagawa, T., Miyoshi, T., Yoshinaga, F., Yamazaki, A. and Mitsugi, K. (1980) Tetrahedron Lett., 21 479
3. Nakanishi, T., Tomita, F. and Suzuki, T. (1974) Agric. Biol. Chem., 38, 2465
4. Iwai, Y., Nakagawa, A., Nagai, A., Matsuyama, K., Takahashi, Y., Yamashita, M., Hirano, A. and Omura, S. (1979) J. Antibiotics, 32, 1367
5. Okawa, N., Nakayama, H., Ikeda, K., Orihata, K., Shimazu, A., Otake, N. and Yonehara, H. (1979) Annual meeting of Kanto Agricultural Chemical Society (Japan), Abst, p 40.
6. Utagawa, T, Morisawa, H., Nakamatsu, T., Yamazaki, A. and Yamanaka, S. Submitted to FEBS Lett. for publication.
7. Ikehara, M., Maruyama, T. and Miki, H. (1976) Tetrahedron Lett. 49, 4485
   Imazawa, M. and Eckstein, F. (1979) J. Org. Chem., 44, 2039
   Hobbs, J. B. and Eckstein, F. (1977) J. Org. Chem.,42, 714
8. Ikehara, M., Maruyama, T. and Miki, H. Tetrahedron, 34, 1133 and references therein.
9. Ikehara, M. and Takatsuka, Y. (1978), Chem. Pharm. Bull. 26 985

3-Methyladenine nucleosides: their synthesis, ring opening, and glycosidic bond cleavage

Tozo Fujii, Tohru Saito and Tsuyoshi Nakasaka

Faculty of Pharmaceutical Sciences, Kanazawa University, Takara-machi, Kanazawa 920, Japan

ABSTRACT

    3-Methyladenosine (Va) and 3-methyl-2'-deoxyadenosine (Vb) have been syn-
thesized in the form of the p-toluenesulfonate salt by methylation of N'-ben-
zyloxy-5-formamido-1-β-D-ribofuranosylimidazole-4-carboxamidine (IIa) and of
N'-benzyloxy-1-(2-deoxy-β-D-ribofuranosyl)-5-formamidoimidazole-4-carboxami-
dine (IIb) followed by hydrogenolysis of the N'-benzyloxy group and cyclization. The 3-methyladenine nucleosides thus obtained are very unstable, and
their hydrolytic cleavage of the glycosidic bond and ring opening of the adenine ring have been studied.

Since methylation of DNA causes release of 3-methyladenine (VI), 3-meth-

yl-2'-deoxyadenosine (Vb) has been assumed to occur in the methylated DNA as

a part structure.[1,2] Because of the extraordinary instability of its glyco-

sidic bond on hydrolysis at the polynucleotide level,[3,4] it would be of prime

importance to learn of the nature of this part structure on the nucleoside

level. We report here the synthesis of 3-methyladenosine (Va)[5] as well as 3-

methyl-2'-deoxyadenosine (Vb) by the application of our general method[5,6] for

the synthesis of 3,9-disubstituted adenines; a comparative study of the be-

havior of the nucleosides (Va,b) and some (Vc,d) of the previously synthesized

3,9-dialkyladenines[6] toward hydrolysis is also included.

    Treatment of the formamidoimidazole IIa,[7] the readily isolable intermedi-

ate in the Dimroth rearrangement of 1-benzyloxyadenosine perchlorate (Ia),[8]

with anhydrous K_2CO_3 and MeI in DMF at room temperature gave the N-methylform-

amido derivative IIIa in 86% yield. Removal of the N'-benzyloxy group from

IIIa was effected by hydrogenolysis (Raney Ni/H_2, 1 atm, room temp., 70 min) in

H_2O in the presence of 1 molar equiv. of p-toluenesulfonic acid (TsOH), and

the crude IVa·TsOH that resulted was treated with a little Et_3N in MeOH at

room temperature for 48 hr to give the desired compound (Va·TsOH),[5] mp ca.

150°C (dec.), in 53% yield from IIIa. 3-Methyl-2'-deoxyadenosine p-toluene-

sulfonate (Vb·TsOH), mp ca. 120°C (dec.), was also synthesized in a similar

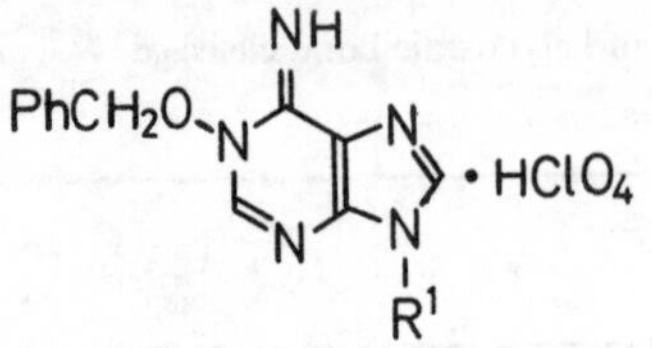

I

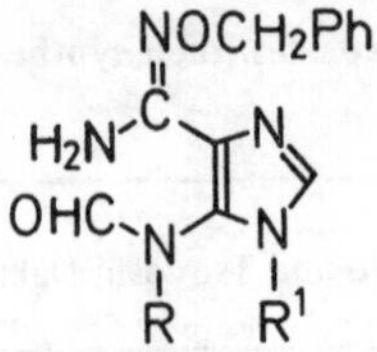

II: R = H

III: R = Me

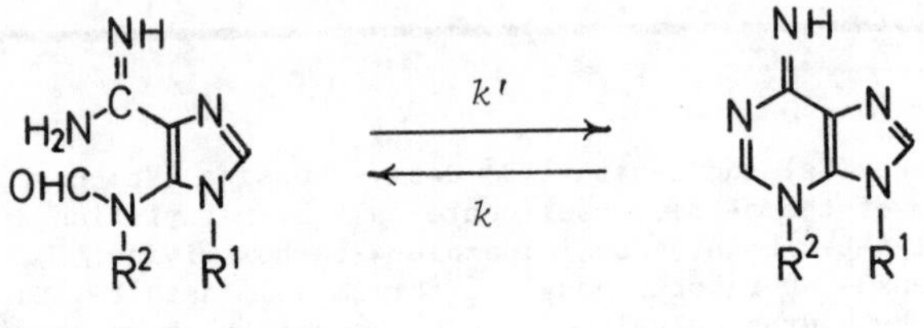

k' / k

IV

V

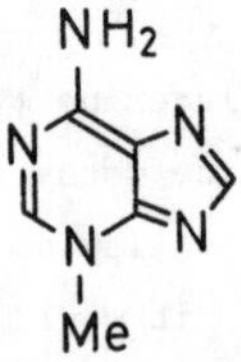

VI

a: R^1 = β-D-ribofuranosyl; R^2 = Me

b: R^1 = 2-deoxy-β-D-ribofuranosyl; R^2 = Me

c: R^1 = Me; R^2 = Me

d: R^1 = Me; R^2 = PhCH$_2$

manner from Ib through IIb,[9] IIIb, and IVb·TsOH.

In contrast to the inertness of the 3,9-dialkyladenine salts (Vc·HCl, Vd·HClO$_4$) in aqueous acidic solution, Va·TsOH and Vb·TsOH separately underwent hydrolysis in H$_2$O at pH 3.34 and 25°C to afford 3-methyladenine (VI)[10] and their hydrolysis rates were determined to be 6.9×10^{-4} min^{-1} (half life 17 hr) and 2.5×10^{-1} min^{-1} (half life 2.7 min). The rates of hydrolyses of Vb·TsOH and methylated DNA[3] at 37°C at pH 5.0 or 7.0 to give VI were also compared.

Under basic conditions the 3-methyladenine nucleosides were also unstable, as in the cases of Vc·HCl and Vd·HClO$_4$. Compounds Va·TsOH, Vc·HCl and Vd·HClO$_4$ came to equilibrium with the ring-opened derivatives IVa, IVc, and IVd, respectively, in H$_2$O at pH 8.98 and 25°C. The pseudo-first-order rate constants and equilibrium constants were determined to be $k = 2.7 \times 10^{-2}$

$\min^{-1}$, $k' = 2.1 \times 10^{-2}$ $\min^{-1}$, and $K = k/k' = 1.3$ for Va $\rightleftharpoons$ IVa; $k = 1.2 \times 10^{-2}$ $\min^{-1}$, $k' = 3.8 \times 10^{-2}$ $\min^{-1}$, and $K = k/k' = 0.32$ for Vc $\rightleftharpoons$ IVc; $k = 1.3 \times 10^{-2}$ $\min^{-1}$, $k' = 0.28 \times 10^{-2}$ $\min^{-1}$, and $K = k/k' = 4.6$ for Vd $\rightleftharpoons$ IVd. The deoxyribofuranosyl analogue Vb·TsOH was also found to undergo ring opening under similar basic conditions. However, the ring opening was accompanied by the slow hydrolytic cleavage of its glycosidic bond to produce VI.

REFERENCES

1. Lawley, P. D. and Brookes, P. (1963) Biochem. J. 89, 127.
2. Riazuddin, S. and Lindahl, T. (1978) Biochemistry 17, 2110, and references cited therein.
3. Margison, G. P. and O'Connor, P. J. (1973) Biochim. Biophys. Acta 331, 349.
4. Maxam, A. A. and Gilbert, W. (1977) Proc. Natl. Acad. Sci. U. S. A. 74, 560.
5. Saito, T. and Fujii, T. (1979) J. Chem. Soc., Chem. Comm. 135.
6. Fujii, T., Saito, T. and Kawanishi, M. (1978) Tetrahedron Lett. 5007.
7. Fujii, T., Wu, C. C., Itaya, T., Moro, S. and Saito, T. (1973) Chem. Pharm. Bull. 21, 1676.
8. Fujii, T., Wu, C. C. and Itaya, T. (1971) Chem. Pharm. Bull. 19, 1368.
9. Montgomery, J. A. and Thomas, H. J. (1972) J. Med. Chem. 15, 182.
10. Jones, J. W. and Robins, R. K. (1962) J. Am. Chem. Soc. 84, 1914.

Nucleic Acids Research

Introduction of substituents to the 7(8)-position of 7-deazaadenosine (tubercidin): conversion to toyocamycin

Shin-ichi Watanabe and Tohru Ueda

Faculty of Pharmaceutical Sciences, Hokkaido University, Sapporo 060, Japan

ABSTRACT
    Treatment of 2',3',5'-tri-O-acetyl-7-deazaadenosine with ClSCN gave the 7-thiocyanato derivative, which was converted to 7-methylthio and 7-methyl-sulfone derivatives. The thio-Claisen rearrangement and desulfurization of 7-allylthio derivative afforded 8-propyl-7-deazaadenosine. The 7-methylsulfone derivative gave the 8-cyano compound by treatment with NaCN. The action of nitrating agent on triacetyltubercidin gave a mixture of the 7- and 8-nitro derivatives. The Mannich reaction of tubercidin gave the 7-morpholinomethyl derivative which was converted to the methyl, formyl, hydroxymethyl, or cyano derivatives in good yield. The conversion of tubercidin to toyocamycin was thus accomplished. Some physical and biological properties of these substituted tubercidins were presented.

INTRODUCTION

    In order to provide derivatives of 7-deazaadenosine (tubercidin, 1) for medicinal interests the electrophilic substitution of the 7(8)-position of 1 was undertaken. Some spectral and biological properties of these derivatives were also investigated.

RESULTS

    Treatment of 2',3',5'-tri-O-acetyl-7-deazaadenosine (2) with thiocyanogen chloride in acetic acid gave a thiocyanato derivative (3). Reduction of 3 with 2-mercaptoethanol followed by methylation afforded the 7-methylthio derivative (4), which was oxidized to give the 7-methylsulfone (5). Attempt to prepare the 7-allylthio derivative from 3 gave a mixture as a result of the thio-Claisen rearrangement, and 8-propyltubercidin (6) was obtained after de-sulfurization followed by deacetylation of the mixture. This sequence of re-action showed that the thiocyanation of 2 had occurred at the 7-position.
    Treatment of 5 with NaCN in dimethylformamide (DMF) afforded the 8-cyano derivative (7), a regio-isomer of toyocamycin. The addition-elimination mecha-

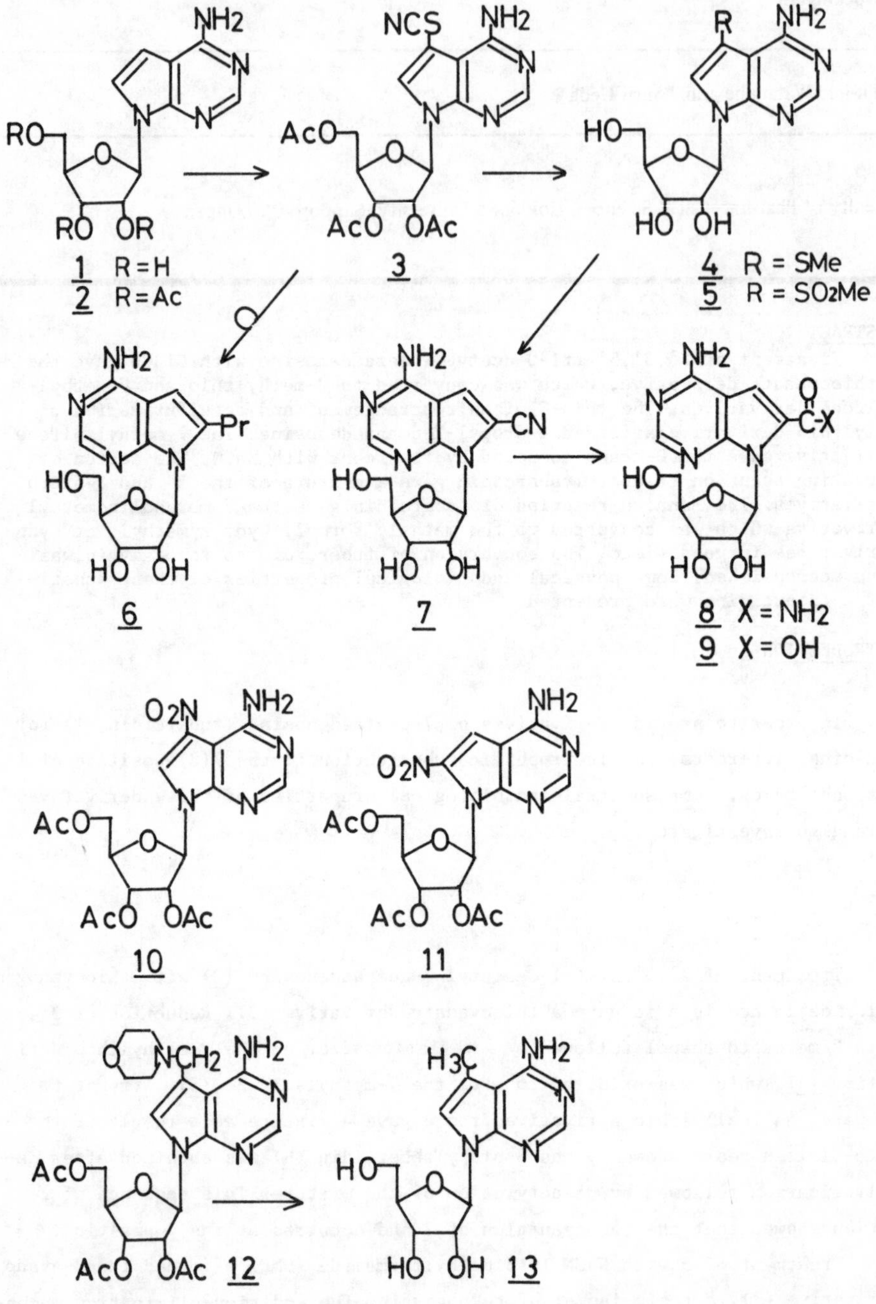
1 R = H
2 R = Ac
3
4 R = SMe
5 R = SO2Me
6
7
8 X = NH2
9 X = OH
10
11
12
13

nism was postulated in the reaction. Compound 7 gave the 7-carboxamide and 8-carboxylic acid (8 and 9) on hydrolysis. Treatment of 2 with f.HNO_3-H_2SO_4 in methylene choride gave a mixture (10 and 11), the major product being the 7-nitro derivative.

For the introduction of a carbon unit into the 7-position of 1 the Mannich reaction was utilized. Heating of 1 with paraformaldehyde and morpholine in DMF, followed by treatment with acetic anhydride afforded a 7-morpholinomethyl derivative (12). Hydrogenation of 12 over Pd-C catalyst gave 7-methyl-7-deazaadenosine (13)[1]. The N-oxidation and successive treatment with acetic acid of the product (14) gave a 7-formyl derivative (15). The oxime formation, dehydration, and deacetylation of 15 furnished toyocamycin (17).

SPECTRAL PROPERTIES

The comparisons of NMR spectra of derivatives of 1 showed that all 8-substituted derivatives tend to possess syn-conformations around the glycosylic linkages, while the 7-substituents did not affect the conformations. The CD spectra of substituted tubercidins also reflected the conformational changes by the 7- or 8-substitution. Similar phenomena have been observed in the 8-substituted adenosines[2].

BIOLOGICAL PROPERTIES

All 7-substituted derivatives of 1, except 13, exhibited weaker activities than that of 1 against <u>Mycobacterium tuberculosis</u> H37Rv. Compound 13 showed comparable activity with 1. Compound 15 showed the highest ILS (69%, at a dose of 10 mg/kg/day x 5) to L 1210 carrying mice. All compounds tested were toxic at the dose of 30 mg/kg.

REFERENCES

1. Kondo, T., Ohgi, T., and Goto, T. (1977) Agr. Biol. Chem., 41, 1501.
2. Matsuda, A., Nomoto, Y., and Ueda, T. (1979) Chem. Pharm. Bull., 27, 183. Nomoto, Y. and Ueda, T. (1980) Abstr. Paper 100th Meeting Pharm. Soc. Japan, p83.

An alternative synthesis of deuterated cytokinins

Tamizi Sugiyama and Takeshi Hashizume

Laboratory of Bioorganic Chemistry, Tokyo Institute of Agriculture and Technology, Fuchu, Tokyo 183, Japan

ABSTRACT

A novel synthesis of penta-deuterated 2-methylthiocytokinins, $(\pm)$-dihydrozeatin, and $(\pm)$-dihydrozeatin riboside is reported. penta-deuterated 2-methylthiocytokinins,2-methylthio-ribosyl-zeatin(I) and N^6-isopentenyl-2-methylthioadenosine (II), were prepared by condensation of amines-d_2 and 6-chloro-2-methylthio-9-β-D-ribo-furanosylpurine-d_3 which was derived from AICA-riboside. The deuterium contents of I and II were 95.75 % and 98.27 %, respectively. Racemic 4-hydroxy-3-methyl-1-butylamine-d_5, which was prepared newly from γ-butyrolactone, was condensed with 6-chloropurine and 6-chloro-9-β-D-ribofuranosylpurine to give racemic dihydrozeatin-d_5(III) and dihydrozeatin riboside-d_5(IV). The deuterium contents were 97.82 % and 97.23 %, respectively.

INTRODUCTION

Deuterated cytokinins have been shown to be an useful inter-nal standard for the determination of endogenous cytokinins by mass spectrometry based on stable-isotope dilution principle.[1,2,3] We previously reported the synthesis of deuterated ribosylzeatin-d_3(RZ-d_3), N^6-isopentenyladenosine-d_6(ipA-d_6), and their 2-methyl-thio derivatives.[1] The deuterium content of 2-methylthio-ribosyl-zeatin-d_3(msRZ-d_3), however, was 82.53 %.[1] In order to increase the deuterium content, msRZ-d_5 was now newly synthesized from 4-hydroxy-3-methyl-2-butenylamine-d_2 and 6-chloro-2-methylthio-9-β-D-ribofuranosylpurine-d_3 possessing methylthio-d_3 group which was prepared via 2-methylthioinosine-d_3 from AICA-riboside. In addition, we synthesized penta-deuterated racemic dihydrozeatin (DHZ-d_5) and dihydrozeatin riboside(DHZR-d_5) by condensation of 4-hydroxy-3-methyl-1-butylamine-d_5 newly prepared from γ-butyro-lactone and 6-chloropurine or its riboside. This paper reports a new synthesis of the deuterated 2-methylthiocytokinins, DHZ-d_5

---

and DHZR-d_5.

RESULTS AND DISCUSSION

The potassium salt of 2-mercaptoinosine was synthesized in 62 % yield from AICA-riboside by the method reported previously[4]. Iodomethane-d_3 (isotopic purity 99.5 Atom % D) was added to the aqueous solution containing the potassium salt to give 2-methylthioinosine-d_3 in 84 % yield. 6-Chloro-2-methylthio-9-β-D-ribofuranosylpurine-d_3 (V) was derived from 2-methylthioinosine-d_3 through three steps involving acetylation, chlorination, and deacetylation in one batch. The overall yield was 63 % when N,N-dimethylformamide-thionyl chloride complex[5] was used for the chlorination of 2',3',5'-tri-O-acetyl-2-methylthioinosine-d_3. Whereas it was only 24 % when phosphorus oxychloride[6] was used. The compound V was identical with the authentic specimen in melting point, NMR and MS spectra.[7] The total extent of deuteration was 98.06 %, and the deuterium distribution was 1.57 % d_1, 1.65 % d_2 and 96.45 % d_3. MsRZ-d_5 (I) was synthesized in 87 % yield by the condensation of V and 4-hydroxy-3-methyl-2-butenylamine-d_2[8]. The total extent of deuteration was 95.75 %, and the deuterium distribution was 0.26 % d_1, 3.21 % d_2, 2.59 % d_3, 5.36 % d_4 and 88.58 % d_5.

MsipA-d_5 (II) was also synthesized in 85 % yield by heating both V and isopentenylamine-d_2[9] in n-butanol. The total extent of deuteration was 98.27 %, and the deuterium distribution was 0.07 % d_1, 0.78 % d_2, 0.61 % d_3, 4.78 % d_4 and 93.76 % d_5. The deuterium content was increased about 5 % more than that of msipA-d_6 reported previously.[1]

4-Hydroxy-3-methyl-1-butylamine-d_5, which constitutes the side chain of DHZ-d_5 and DHZR-d_5, was prepared from γ-butyrolactone through four steps. Methylation of γ-butyrolactone was carried out with iodomethane-d_3 in the presence of lithium diisopropylamide to give α-methyl-γ-butyrolactone-d_3 (VI), $[\alpha]_D^{28} + 0.05$, in 78 % yield by the method reported previously.[11] Ethyl 4-bromo-2-methylbutylate-d_3, which was prepared from VI in anhydrous ethanol saturated with hydrogen bromide, was derived to ethyl 4-azide-2-methylbutylate-d_3 (VII) with sodium azide in 85 % aqueous ethanol. Reduction of VII with lithium aluminum deuteride (isotopic

purity 99 Atom % D) in ether solution yielded 4-hydroxy-3-methyl-1-butylamine-d_5, which was crystallized as oxalate(VIII).[11]
The overall yield of VIII from γ-butyrolactone was 32 %. Racemic VIII was condensed with 6-chloropurine in n-butanol containing triethylamine, followed by purification with silica-gel column chromatography to give ($\pm$)-DHZ-d_5(III) in 77 % yield. The total extent of deuteration was 97.82 %, and the deuterium distribution was 0.30 % d_1, 0.59 % d_2, 1.09 % d_3, 5.74 % d_4 and 92.28 % d_5.

Similarly, the reaction of racemic VIII with 6-chloro-9-β-D-ribofuranosylpurine afforded ($\pm$)-DHZR-d_5(IV) in 73 % yield. The total extent of deuteration was 97.23 %, and the deuterium distribution was 0.49 % d_1, 0.33 % d_2, 0.98 % d_3, 8.99 % d_4 and 89.22 % d_5.

	R_1	R_2	R_3
I =	$-CH_2CH=C\begin{smallmatrix}CH_3\\CD_2OH\end{smallmatrix}$	SCD_3	ribose
II =	$-CD_2CH=C(CH_3)_2$	SCD_3	ribose
III =	$-CH_2CH_2\underset{CD_3}{C}HCD_2OH$	H	H
IV =	$-CH_2CH_2\underset{CD_3}{C}HCD_2OH$	H	ribose

In the quantitative determination of endogenous cytokinins in biological samples by using selected ion-monitoring technique, the content of d_0 component in the deuterated internal standard should be in the lowest level. From this viewpoint, the penta-deuterated cytokinins synthesized here appear to be favorable internal standard.

REFERENCES

1, Hashizume.T, Sugiyama,T., Imura,M., Cory,H.T., Scott,M.F., and McCloskey,J.A.(1979) Anal. Biochem. 92, 111.
2, McCloskey,J.A., Hashizume,T., Basile,B., Sugiyama,T., and Sekiguchi,S.(1979) Proc. Japan Acad. 55, ser. B, 445.
3, McCloskey,J.A., Hashizume,T., Basile,B., Ohno,Y., and Sonoki,S.(1980) FEBS Letts. 111, 181.
4, Imai,K., Marumoto,R., Kobayashi,K., Yoshida,Y., Toda,Y., and Honjo,M.(1971) Chem. Pharm. Bull. 19, 576.

5, Ikehara,M., Uno,H., and Ishihara,F.(1964) Chem. Pharm. Bull. 12, 267.
6, Gester,J.F., Jones,J.W., and Robins,R.K.(1963) J. Org. Chem. 28, 945.
7, Sugiyama,T., and Hashizume,T,(1978) Agric. Biol. Chem. 42, 1791.
8, Shaw,G., Smallwood,B.H., and Wilson,D.V.(1966) J.Chem. Soc. 924.
9, Hall,R.H., Fleysher,M.H.(1968) in Synthetic Procedures in Nucleic Acid Chemistry, Vol. I, pp. 517, Wily-Interscience, New York.
10, Herrmann,J.L., and Schlessinger,R.H.(1973) Chem. Commun. 711.
11, Adams,R., and Fles,D.(1959) J. Amer. Chem. Soc. 81, 4946.

A facile and regiospecific preparation of 6-alkyluridines

Hiromichi Tanaka, Ikuyo Nasu, Hiroyuki Hayakawa and Tadashi Miyasaka

School of Pharmaceutical Sciences, Showa University, Hatanodai 1-5-8, Shinagawa-ku, Tokyo 142, Japan

ABSTRACT

2',3'-O-Isopropylideneuridine, upon lithiation and subsequent alkylation, was transformed to 6-alkyl derivatives in a regiospecific manner. After acidic treatment of the acetonides, 6-alkyluridines (methyl, ethyl, propyl, isopropyl, butyl, sec-butyl, and hexan-3-yl) were obtained. 5'-Deoxy-6-alkyluridines (methyl, ethyl, and isopropyl) were also prepared by the same route from 5'-deoxy-2',3'-O-isopropylideneuridine.

INTRODUCTION

Though methodology has evolved for the synthesis of various nucleosides, very few example has been reported for the preparation of 6-alkylpyrimidine nucleosides[1] which might be expected to have antiviral activity[2] and to serve as a useful model to elucidate the glycosidic conformation.[3] As a part of our studies on the conversion of naturally occurring nucleosides to physiologically active derivatives,[4] introduction of alkyl substituent to the 6-position of uridine was investigated.

RESULTS

While the most straightforward route to introduce alkyl group to uracil ring would be the metalation-alkylation reaction sequence, the lithiation of tris-trimethylsilyluridine with butyllithium is known to occur at both C-5 and C-6.[5]

In the present case, however, when 2',3'-O-isopropylidene-uridine (1) was treated with lithium diisopropylamide (LDA) in tetrahydrofuran at -78°C, lithiation took place regiospecifically at C-6 (deutrium incorporation was estimated at approximately 70% by PMR after quenching with CH₃COOD).

The reaction of the lithio derivative (2) with methyl

iodide was then carried out at -78°C for 2 h. Quenching with acetic acid followed by chromatographic purification of the resulting mixture gave 6-methyl-2',3'-O-isopropylideneuridine (3a) in 46% yield as crystals (mp 155~156°). The additional two products 3b and 3c were obtained especially when the above reaction was performed on a large scale (10 mmol or more of 1).

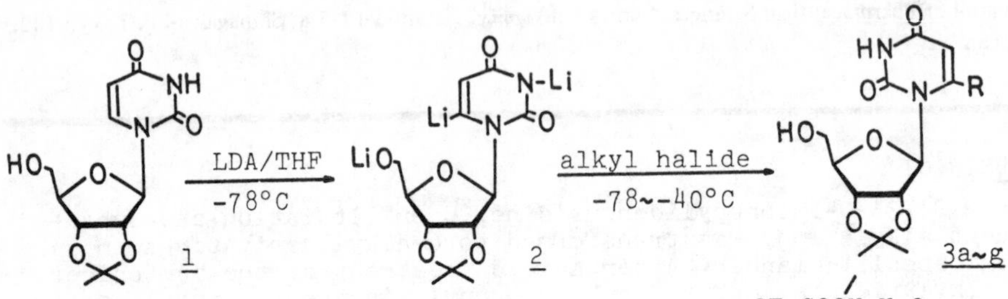

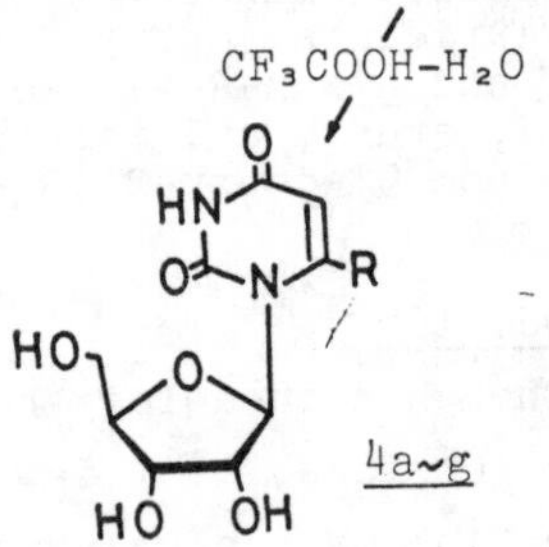

	R	mp(°C) of 4
a	methyl	184.5~186.5
b	ethyl	foam
c	isopropyl	204~206
d	propyl	177~178
e	butyl	152~154
f	sec-butyl	198.5~200
g	hexan-3-yl	foam

Similar reactions with other primary alkyl bromides (ethyl, propyl, and butyl) at -40°C for 14 h were also successful to furnish the corresponding 6-alkyl derivatives (3b,d,e) in 40~ 60% yields, together with a small amount of the secondary alkyl-ated products except in the case of butyl bromide.

It would be noteworthy that, even in the presence of excess alkylating agent, neither N^3-position nor 5'-hydroxyl group was alkylated under the aforementioned conditions. Treatment of the acetonides(3) with aqueous trifluoroacetic acid gave rise to the desired free nucleosides (4) in virtually quantitative yields.

We initially considered the possibility that the 5'-hydro-xyl group could participate in the stabilization of the 6-lithio derivative (2) leading to the regiospecific metalation,[6] but discount this possibility, since the same conversion with 5'-deoxy-2',3'-O-isopropylideneuridine (5, R=H) using methyl iodide resulted in the exclusive formation of the 6-alkyl substituted products (5a~c). Deblocking of 5a~c afforded the diols (6a~c).

	R
a	methyl
b	ethyl
c	isopropyl

5a~c (R',R"=isopropylidene)
6a~c (R'=R"=H)

TABLE 1　B_{2u} molecular ellipticities of 6-alkyluridine derivatives in methanol

R	4	3	6	5
H	+10800	+6700	+11000	+4100
methyl	-300	-700	-400	-1300
ethyl	-500	-1300	-600	-2800
isopropyl	-600	-1700	-800	-3100
propyl	-700	-1500		
butyl	-700	-1500		
sec-butyl *	-1400	-1400		
hexan-3-yl*	-1600	-1400		

* probably epimeric mixture

In Table 1 is summarized the B_{2u} molecular ellipticity of nucleosides involved in the present study.

All 6-substituted uridines (4a~g) including 5'-deoxy analogues (6a~c) exhibited weak negative ellipticities contrary to that of uridine and 5'-deoxyuridine, and the bulkiness of substituent has little effect on the CD spectra. Though the electronic effect of an alkyl substituent should not be set aside, the negative B_{2u} ellipticities of 6-alkylated nucleosides may well be assigned to a sterically required syn conformation.[3]

The authors gratefully acknowledge Professor T. Ueda, Faculty of Pharmaceutical Sciences, Hokkaido University, for the use of a CD instrument and helpful suggestions.

REFERENCES
1 Fourrey, J.L., Henry, G., and Jouin, P. (1979) Tetrahedron Lett., 951-954, and references cited therein.
2 Diwan, A.R., Robins, R.K., and Prusoff, W.H. (1969) Experientia, 25, 98-100.
3 a) Miles, D.W., Robins, M.J., Robins, R.K., Winkley, M.W., and Erying, H. (1969) J. Am. Chem. Soc., 91, 824-831, 831-838; b) Schweizer, M.P., Banta, E.B., Witkowski, J.T., and Robins, R.K. (1973) ibid., 95, 3770-3778.

4 Miyasaka, T., Suemune, H., and Arakawa, K.(the late) (1978)
  Nucleic Acids Symposium series, No. 5, s273-276, and loc. cit.
5 Pichat, L., Godbillon, J., and Herbert, M. (1973) Bull. Soc.
  Chim. Fr., 2715-2719.
6 Tanaka, H., Nasu, I., and Miyasaka, T. (1979) Tetrahedron
  Lett., 4755-4758.

Nucleic Acids Research

Synthesis and antiherpesviral activity of 5-C-substituted uracil nucleosides

Shinji Sakata[*], Susumu Shibuya[*], Haruhiko Machida[*], Hiroshi Yoshino[*], Kosaku Hirota[**], Shigeo Senda[**], Kazuyoshi Ikeda[+] and Yoshihisa Mizuno[†]

[*]Research Laboratory, Yamasa Shoyu Co. Ltd., Choshi 288, [**]Gifu College of Pharmacy, Gifu 502, [+]Center for Instrumental Analysis, and [†]Faculty of Pharmaceutical Sciences, Hokkaido University, Sapporo 060, Japan

ABSTRACT

Reaction of 2'-deoxy-5-hydroxyuridine with some Wittig reagents gave 5-alkoxycarbonylmethyl-, 5-carbamoylmethyl-, 5-cyanomethyl-and 5-acetonyl-2'-deoxyuridines. The corresponding 1-β-D-arabinofuranosyl derivatives were prepared from 1-β-D-arabinofuranosyl-5-hydroxymethyluracil. The latter was also converted to 1-β-D-arabinofuranosyl-5-vinyluracil via triphenylphos-phonium salt, and then to 5-(2-halogenovinyl)derivatives. Some of these compounds showed marked antiherpesviral activity in vitro.

INTRODUCTION

Modifications at the 5-position of pyrimidine deoxyribo- and arabino-nucleosides have produced a number of compounds with selective biological activity[1]. Recently, De Clercq et al[2] reported highly inhibitory action of E-5-(2-bromovinyl)-2'-deoxyuridine against herpes simplex virus (HSV). We also showed that some of 5-alkyl and 5-alkenyl derivatives of 1-β-D-arabino-furanosyluracil effectively inhibited HSV multiplication without any signifi-cant action against cell growth[3,4]. We wish to describe here the synthesis and antiviral activity of new compounds containing two carbons unit at the 5-position of 2'-deoxyuridine and 1-β-D-arabinofuranosyluracil, and indicate highly selective inhibition of HSV multiplication by 1-β-D-arabinofuranosyl-E-5-(2-halogenovinyl)uracils.

RESULTS

The reaction of 5-hydroxyuracils with Wittig reagents reported by Senda et al[5] was applied to synthesis 5-substituted 2'-deoxyuridines. 2'-Deoxy-5-hydroxyuridine(1) was treated with ethoxycarbonylmethylenetriphenylphosphorane in dioxane under reflux for 3 hr to give 2'-deoxy-5-ethoxycarbonylmethyluridine (4) in 80% yield. Treatment of 1 with several other stable phosphoranes gave the corresponding 5-substituted 2'-deoxyuridines (3,5,6,7) in good yield.

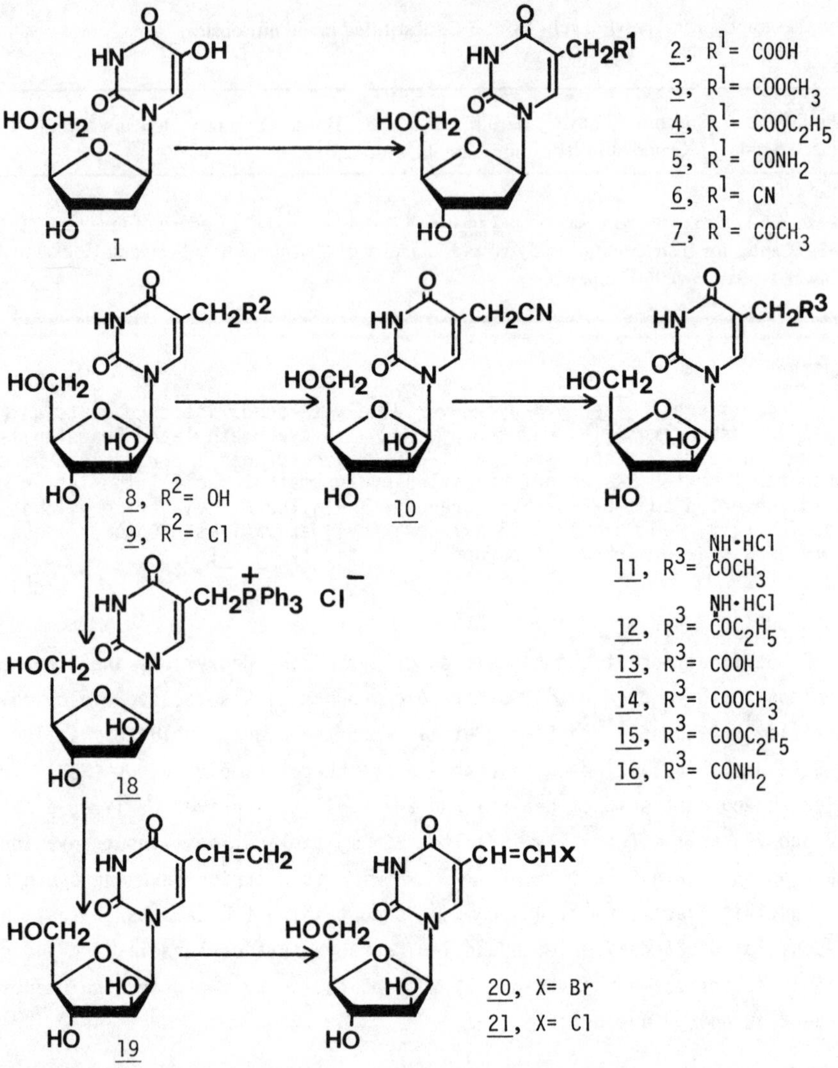

2, R^1 = COOH
3, R^1 = COOCH$_3$
4, R^1 = COOC$_2$H$_5$
5, R^1 = CONH$_2$
6, R^1 = CN
7, R^1 = COCH$_3$

8, R^2 = OH
9, R^2 = Cl

11, R^3 = $\overset{NH \cdot HCl}{\overset{\|}{C}}OCH_3$
12, R^3 = $\overset{NH \cdot HCl}{\overset{\|}{C}}OC_2H_5$
13, R^3 = COOH
14, R^3 = COOCH$_3$
15, R^3 = COOC$_2$H$_5$
16, R^3 = CONH$_2$

20, X = Br
21, X = Cl

Alkaline hydrolysis of 4 afforded 5-carboxymethyl-2'-deoxyuridine(2).

1-β-D-Arabinofuranosyl-5-chloromethyluracil(9) prepared from 5-hydroxy-methyl derivative(8) was treated with sodium cyanide in aqueous dimethylform-amide to give 5-cyanomethyl derivative(10) in 48% yield. Alcoholysis of 10 with anhydrous acidic conditions at room temperature gave acetimino ethers (11 and 12) in high yield. Acetimino ethers were readily hydrolyzed to ace-tates: treatment of 11 with water at room temperature for 1 hr afforded methyl ester(14) in 66% yield, and treatment of 12 with ethanol under reflux

Table 1. Melting point and biological activity of the products

| Compound | mp (°C) | Anti-HSV-1 activity | | Antiviral index** |
		Virus rating	MIC*(µg/ml)	
5-I-dUrd[a]		2.4	3.2	2.5
5-CH$_3$-araUra (ara-T)[a]		2.7	1.0	100 - 150
5-CH$_2$COOH-dUrd($\underline{2}$)	220 - 223	0.6	320	
5-CH$_2$COOCH$_3$-dUrd($\underline{3}$)	156 - 157	1.3	32	
5-CH$_2$COOC$_2$H$_5$-dUrd($\underline{4}$)	186 - 187	1.1	100	
5-CH$_2$CN-dUrd($\underline{6}$)	201 - 202	0.1	>1,000	
5-CH$_2$CONH$_2$-dUrd($\underline{5}$)	220 - 222	0.4	1,000	
5-CH$_2$COCH$_3$-dUrd($\underline{7}$)	170 - 171	2.0	3.2	>156
5-CH$_2$COOH-araUra($\underline{13}$)	235	0	>1,000	
5-CH$_2$COOCH$_3$-araUra($\underline{14}$)	134 - 137	0.6	320	
5-CH$_2$COOC$_2$H$_5$-araUra($\underline{15}$)	160 - 163	0.1	>1,000	
5-CH$_2$CN-araUra($\underline{10}$)	228.5	0.8	100	
5-CH$_2$CONH$_2$-araUra($\underline{16}$)	232 - 233	0.1	>1,000	
5-CH$_2$COCH$_3$-araUra($\underline{17}$)	179 - 180	0.5	320	
5-CH=CH$_2$-araUra($\underline{19}$)[b]		2.7	1.0	620
5-CH=CHBr-araUra($\underline{20}$)	182	3.7	0.032	>15,600
5-CH=CHCl-araUra($\underline{21}$)	221.5	3.0	0.1	>5,000

* Minimum inhibitory concentration at which virus-induced cytopathogenic effect was depressed more than 50%.

** The ID$_{50}$ against HEL-F cell-growth divided by the MIC against HSV-1.

a) See ref. 3. b) See ref. 4.

for 10 min afforded ethyl ester($\underline{15}$) in 73% yield. Hydrolysis of $\underline{14}$ with 1N-HCl at 80°C for 2 hr gave 5-acetic acid($\underline{13}$) in 92% yield. Treatment of $\underline{15}$ with methanolic ammonia at room temperature for 72 hr afforded 5-acetamide ($\underline{16}$) in 72% yield. 5-Acetonyluridine prepared from 5-hydroxyuridine was treated with diphenyl carbonate in dimethylformamide to give 5-acetonyl-0^2, 2'-cyclouridine, which was converted to 5-acetonyl-1-β-D-arabinofuranosyl-uracil($\underline{17}$) by acid hydrolysis in 48% yield.

Compound($\underline{9}$) was converted to triphenylphosphonium salt($\underline{18}$), which was further treated with butyllithium and paraformaldehyde to give 1-β-D-arabinofuranosyl-5-vinyluracil(19) by the method reported previously[6]. Bromination of 19 with bromine in dimethylformamide at 100° for 2 hr, or with N-bromosuccinimide in dimethylformamide at room temperature for 4.5 hr gave 1-β-D-arabinofuranosyl-E-5-(2-bromovinyl)uracil(20) in 60% or 20% yield. Similarly E-5-(2-chlorovinyl) derivative(21) was obtained by treating 19 with chlorine or N-chlorosuccinimide. The assignment of the E-configuration around the exocyclic double bond of these compounds was based on the coupling constant (J=13 Hz) of the vinylic protons. These coupling constants (J=13.5 Hz in 20, J=13.0 Hz in 21) were found to be in good agreement with data reported for E-5-(2-bromovinyl)uracil[7] and its 2'-deoxyribofuranosyl derivative[8].

Antiherpesviral activity of the compounds synthesized was determined by a modified virus rating method using human embryonic lung fibroblast (HEL-F) cells, HSV type 1 (HSV-1) and HSV type 2 (HSV-2) as described previously[3]. As shown in Table 1, 7, 20 and 21, as well as 2'-deoxy-5-iodouridine, 1-β-D-arabinofuranosylthymine and 19, were highly active against HSV-1. However, 7, 20 and 21 were weakly or not active against HSV-2. 5-Substituted arabino-furanosyluracils were generally less active against HSV-1 than the corresponding derivatives of deoxyuridine except that 10 was more active than 6. Several compounds active against HSV-1 were tested for anti-cell growth activity. All compounds tested were not inhibitory to growth of HEL-F cells, exhibiting a wide margin of safety (Table 1).

REFERENCES
1. De Clercq, E. and Torrence, P.F.(1978) J.Carbohydr. Nucleosides Nucleotides, 5, 187-224
2. De Clercq, E., Descamps, J., De Somer, P., Barr, P.J., Jones, A.S. and Walker, R.T.(1979) Proc. Natl. Acad. Sci. USA, 76, 2947-2951
3. Machida, H., Sakata, S., Kuninaka, A., Yoshino, H., Nakayama, C. and Saneyoshi, M.(1979) Antimicrob. Agents Chemother., 16, 158-163
4. Machida, H., Kuninaka, A., Yoshino, H., Ikeda, K. and Mizuno, Y.(1980) Antimicrob. Agents Chemother., 17, (in press)
5. Senda, S., Hirota, K., Asao, T. and Suematsu, M.(1979) Abst. Papers 99th Ann. Meet. Pharm. Soc. Japan, p.213
6. Ikeda, K., Takatsuki, Y., Mizuno, Y. and Machida, H.(1979) Abst. Papers 99th Ann. Meet. Pharm. Soc. Japan, p.213
7. Bleackley, R.C., Jones, A.S. and Walker, R.T.(1976) Tetrahedron, 32, 2975-2977
8. Jones, A.S., Verhelst, G. and Walker, R.T.(1979) Tetrahedron Lett., 4415-4418

Halogenation of 6-O-cyclouracil nucleosides

Tokumi Maruyama and Mikio Honjo

School of Pharmacy, Tokushima University of Arts and Science, Yamashiro-cho, Tokushima 770, Japan

ABSTRACT

Bromination or iodination at the 5-position of 6-O-cyclo-uracil nucleosides was effected in a fairly good yield. Besides monohalogenated nucleosides, there were prepared novel dibromo compounds, which were assigned the structures, 5,5-di-bromo-6,6-di-O-cyclouracil nucleosides (VI, VIII).

Halogenation of pyrimidine nucleosides is a useful process to provide a wide variety of interesting nucleoside analogs; they often have valuable biological properties.

We treated 6:2'-O-cyclouracil arabinoside (I) and 6:3'-O-cyclouracil xyloside[1] (II) with iodine in the presence of iodic acid[2] to prepare the corresponding 5-iodo derivatives (IV, V) in good yields, respectively.

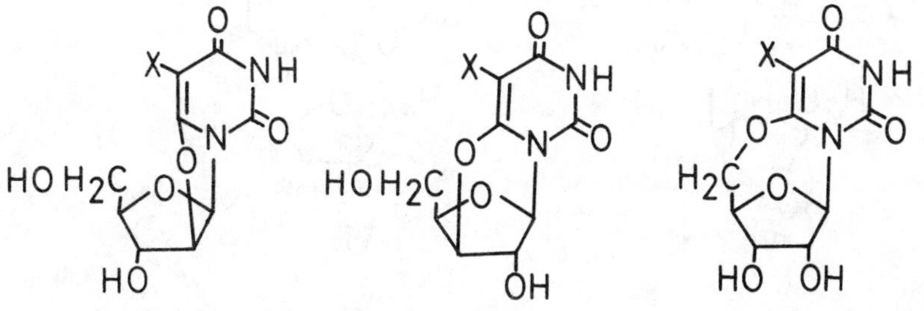

I ; X = H
IV ; X = I
VII ; X = Br

II ; X = H
V ; X = I

III ; X = H
IX ; X = I
X ; X = Br

Treatment of I with aqueous solution of bromine[3] at room temperature afforded two compounds. A major product was isolated from the reaction mixture. The structure was determined to be 6:2',6:5'-dianhydro-5,5-dibromo-6,6-dihydroxy-5,6-dihydro-uracil arabinoside (VI), on the basis of elemental analysis, mass and nuclear magnetic resonance spectra. A minor product, which was isolated by successive treatment of the mother liquor, was proved to be 5-bromo derivative (VII) of I. The intramolecu-lar 6:5'-O-cyclization is presumed to be caused by nucleophilic attack of the 5'-hydroxyl group on the 6-position of VII. The position might be electron-deficient owing to electrophilic at-tack of the bromium cation on the 5,6-double bond of VII. This interpretation receives support from the fact that the reaction of VII with aqueous solution of bromine led to the formation of VI.

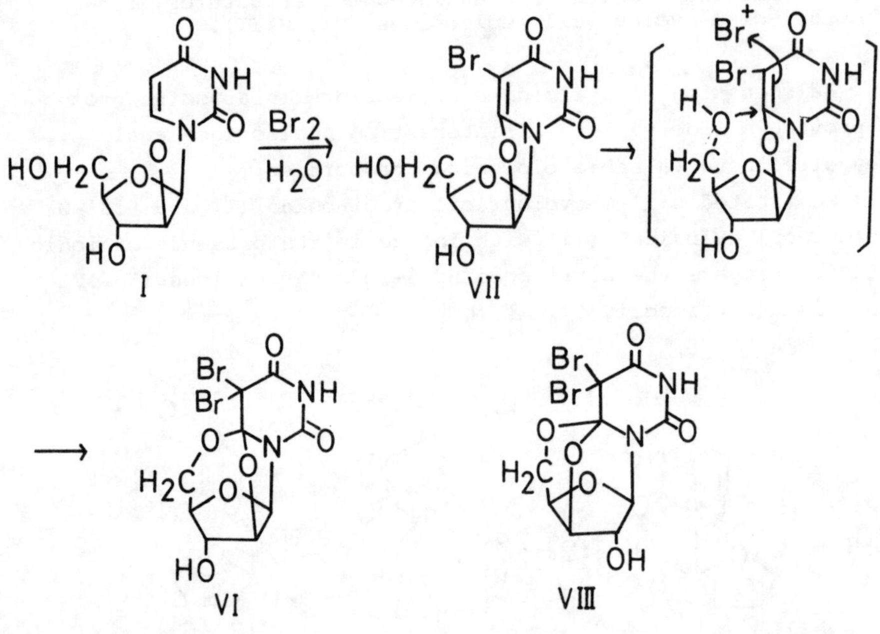

A similar bromination of II afforded the corresponding 6:3',6:5'-di-O-cyclo compound (VIII). These are the first to pre-pare the di-O-cyclonucleosides.

Iodination or bromination of 6:5'-O-cyclouridine (III) under the above-described conditions gave a complicated result. This might be attributed to the side reactions including the O-cyclic bond fission of III, because the bond is more labile to acid than that of I or II.[1] The synthesis of 5-iodo (IX) or 5-bromo derivative (X) was thus achieved in a fairly good yield by halogenation of 2',3'-di-O-benzoyl derivative of III with N-iodosuccinimide[4] or N-bromosuccinimide[5], followed by treatment with methanolic ammonia, respectively.

REFERENCES

1. Maruyama,T. and Honjo,M.(1979) Nucleic Acids Research, Symposium Series No. 6, s7
2. (a) Chang,P.K.(1965) J. Org. Chem, 30, 3913; (b) Honjo,M., Furukawa,Y., Nishikawa,M., Kamiya,K. and Yoshioka,Y.(1967) Chem. Phar. Bull., 15, 1076
3. (a) Levene,P.A. and La Forge,F.B.(1912) Chem. Ber., 45, 608; (b) Fukuhara,T.K. and Visser,D.W.(1951) J. Biol. Chem., 190, 95
4. Lipkin,D. and Rabi,J.A.(1971) J. Amer. Chem. Soc., 93, 3309
5. Michelson,A.M.(1958) J. Chem. Soc., 1957

Synthesis of naturally occurring uridine-α-amino acid derivatives by the application of Ugi reaction

Kiyomi Tsuchida[*], Yoshihisa Mizuno[*] and Kazuyoshi Ikeda[**]

[*]Faculty of Pharmaceutical Sciences, and [**]Center of Instrumental Analysis, Hokkaido University, Sapporo 060, Japan

Abstract

A simultaneous condensation (Ugi reaction) of four components (aldehyde, amine, isocyanide, and carboxylic acid) may be a useful reaction for the construction of N,N'-disubstituted α-aminocarboxamide structure. We have found that the reaction involving (2-picolyl 1-oxide) amine (op-amine) gave rise to a product, one of whose nitrogen-substitutent could be easily removed to give mono-substituted derivative. Thus, the polyoxin skeleton as well as 3-(3-amino-3-carboxypropyl) uridine (a modified nucleoside in certain t-RNAs) were synthesized by the Ugi reaction by the use of the "op"-amine and appropriate aldehyde derived from uridine. Attempted synthesis of these nucleoside derivatives by the condensation involving (2-picolyl 1-oxide) isocyanide as well as the "op"-amine will be also touched on briefly.

Out of a large number of naturally occurring nucleosides, 3-(3-amino-3-carboxypropyl) uridine[1] (1) and polyoxins[2] [for instance, 2(R=CH$_2$OH)] are

unique in that the structures may be constructed (at least formally) by a combination of nucleosides and amino acids moiety. Chemical syntheses of these hybrids of nucleosides and amino acids have been achieved by a number of workers.[3], [4]

However, as a part of our continuing synthetic studies of natural products

by application of four component condensation[5] involving amines and iso-
cyanides of 2-picolyl 1-oxide series[6], the synthesis of these nucleosides[1
and 2 (R=H)] was attempted by the use of this condensation reaction as a key
step.

Synthesis of 3-(3-amino-3-carboxypropyl)uridine (1)

Synthetic sequence of our approach to 1 is shown in accompanying scheme 1.
2',3'-O-Isopropylidenuridine (3) was reacted with 3-bromopropanal diethyl
acetal in DMF in the presence of potassium carbonate. After usual work-up including silica gel column chromatography, 3-(3,3-diethoxypropyl)uridine derivative (4) was obtained in a quantitative yield. The structure was confirmed by nmr and mass spectroscopy [ms(m/e) 399 (M^+-15)]. Hydrolysis of 4 in
dioxane-0.2N HCl (1:1) at room temperature for 3.5 hr afforded the corresponding aldehyde(5). Nmr(CDCl$_3$) δ 9.75 ppm(s, 1H, CH=O); ms(m/e) 325 (M^+-15).
5 was allowed to react with "op"-amine (2-picolyl 1-oxide will be referred to
as "op", hereafter), cyclohexenylisocyanide[7], and acetic acid (whose molar
ratios; 1:1:1) in MeOH-CH$_2$Cl$_2$ at room temperature for 24 hr to afford a
crude product(6). The structure was confirmed by the presence of cyclohexenyl,
"op", acetyl and isopropylidene group in nmr spectra. Removal of the cyclohexenyl group in 6 could be effected by treatment with 50% aq AcOH at room
temperature for 38 hr. The structure was confirmed by spectral data, [ms(m/e)
515 (M^+-18); nmr (CDCl$_3$) spectra showed the presence of "op", CH$_3$CO-, and
isopropylidene group]. Its combustion values were also in keeping with the
structure assigned. Treatment of 7 with excess acetic anhydride at 40° for 18
hr, followed by separation by the aid of column afforded 8, which in turn
was treated with ethanolic ammonia at room temperature for 18 hr. Work-up including silica gel column chromatography afforded 9 as a foam. Ms(m/e) 426
(M^+); 411 (M^+-15); nmr (CDCl$_3$) spectral data was also consistent with the
structure assigned. Hydrolysis of isopropylidene group in 9 by conventional
method (50% aq. AcOH, 100°, 1 hr) afforded, after recrystallization, an analytical sample of 10, mp 124-130° (dec.), yield being 75%. Solvolysis of 10
with absolute methanol in the presence of Dowex 50W (H$^+$ form) at 37° for 40 hr
gave rise to 11. Nmr (DMSO-d$_6$) δ 3.61 (3H, s, OCH$_3$). Ms(m/e) 401 (M^+), 342 (M^+-
CO$_2$CH$_3$). The structure assigned was also consistent with combustion values.

9 was treated with 6N HCl at 80° for 1.5 hr. The ninhydrin-test positive
fraction was isolated by cellulose column chromatography. UVλmax (264 nm) of
the product did not shift in H$_2$O, acidic and alkaline media. The compound had

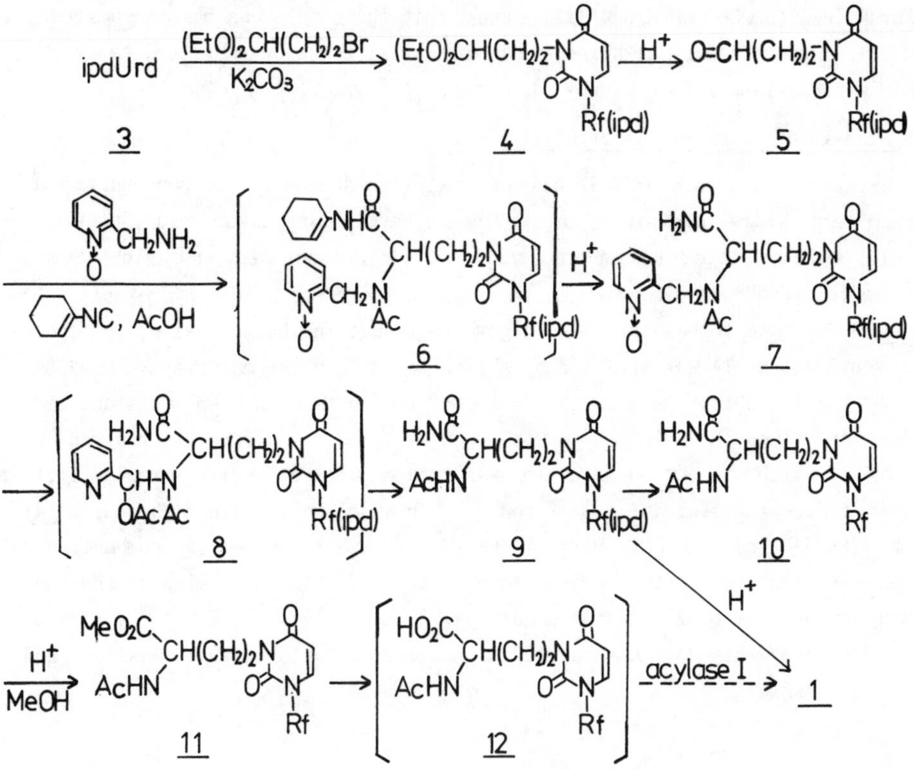

Rf = 1-β-D-ribofuranosyl   Rf(ipd)= 2',3'-O-isopropyridene-Rf

Scheme 1

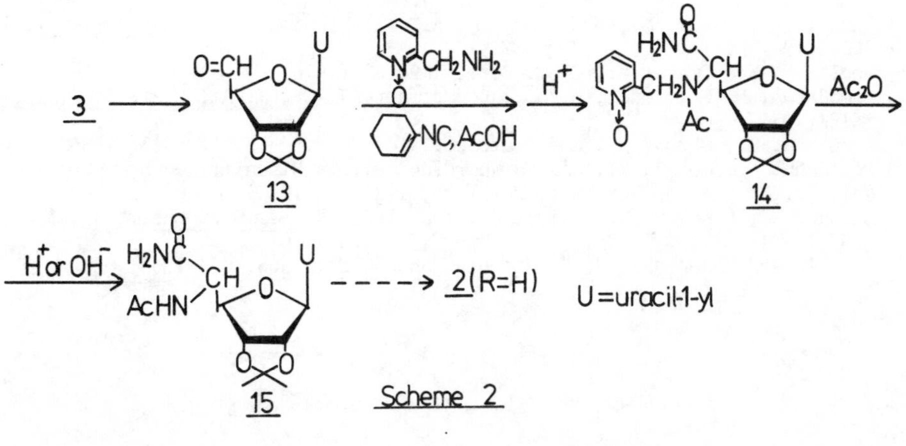

U=uracil-1-yl

Scheme 2

a mobility (PEP. 0.05M TEAB, pH 7.5) of 7 cm, compared to a mobility of 4.5 cm for 9. PPC (BuOH-AcOH-H_2O 4:1:2) showed that the sample was homogeneous (Rf 0.23). 12 obtained by alkaline hydrolysis of 11 is being subjected to hydrolysis with acylase 1 (pig kidney) in order to resolute the racemate.

Synthesis of Polyoxin Skeleton (2)

Synthetic sequence of 2 is also shown in the scheme 2. The condensation at room temperature, overnight, of "op"-amine, cyclohexenylisocyanide, acetic acid, and Moffatt oxidation product from 2',3'-O-isopropylidenuridine gave rise to a crude sample which in turn was subjected to acidic hydrolysis (50% aq. AcOH, room temperature, overnight) to result in the removal of the cyclohexenyl group. 14 was isolated by silica gel column chromatography. Mp 258-259° (yield, 29%). The structure was confirmed both by nmr analysis and combustion values. Reaction of 14 with Ac_2O (45°, 42 hr) afforded a rearranged product which without purification was treated with ethanolic ammonia (1:1) at room temperature for 1.5 hr. 15 could be obtained in 84% yield (based on 14). Mp 228-235° (dec., MeOH). Ms(m/e) 368 (M^+). Nmr data as well as combustion values was consistent with the structure, assigned. Attempt aiming at the conversion of 15 into 2 is being under way.

A part of this work was carried out in collaboration with Y. Kakizaki and K. Kobayashi.

References

1 Barrell, B. G. and Sanger, F., FEBS Lett., 3, 275 (1969)
  Friedman, S., Li Janet, H., Nakanishi, K., and Van Lear, G., Biochemistry, 13, 2932 (1974)
2 Isono, K., Asahi, K., and Suzuki, S., J. Am. Chem. Soc., 91, 7490 (1969)
3 Ohashi, Z., Maeda, M., McCloskey, J. A., and Nishimura, S., Biochemistry, 13, 2620 (1974)
  Seela, F. and Cramer F., Chem. Ber., 109, 82 (1976)
4 Damodaran, N. P., Jones, G. H., and Moffatt, J. G., J. Am. Chem. Soc., 93, 3812 (1971)
  Kuzuhara, H., Ohrui, H., and Emoto, S., Tetrahedron Lett., 1973, 5055
5 Hoffmann, P., Gokel, G., and Marquarding, D., in "Isonitrile Chemistry", Ugi, I., Ed., Academic Press, New York, 1971, pp 19-35
6 Mizuno, Y., Limn, W., Tsuchida, K., and Ikeda, K., J. Org. Chem., 37, 39 (1972)
7 Ugi, I. and Rosendahl, F. K., Liebigs Ann. Chem., 666, 65 (1963)

Use of α-secondary isotope effects in nucleophile-promoted reactions of pyrimidine derivatives; evidence for transient 5,6-dihydropyrimidine intermediates

Yusuke Wataya[*], Reiko Kawada[*], Atsuko Itadani[*], Hikoya Hayatsu[*], Thomas W.Bruice[**], Charles Garrett[**], Akira Matsuda[**] and Daniel V.Santi[**]

[*]Faculty of Pharmaceutical Sciences, Okayama University, Okayama 700, Japan, and [**]Department of Biochemistry and Biophysics and Department of Pharmaceutical Chemistry, University of California, San Francisco, CA 94143, USA

SUMMARY

α-Secondary isotope effect provides a useful tool for detection of transient 5,6-dihydropyrimidine intermediates which have been indirectly implicated in a number of chemical and enzymic conversions of pyrimidine heterocycles. The method involves the use of kinetic secondary α-hydrogen isotope effects which are expected to accompany sp^2 to sp^3 rehybridization of C-6 of the pyrimidine ring if they occur prior to or at the rate determining step. Thus, using 6-tritiated pyrimidines, and measurement of the isotopic ratio of reactant and products, k_T/k_H values of 1.15 or greater would be indicative of rehybridization. Using this method, we have studied the inhibition of thymidylate synthetase by 5-fluorodeoxyuridylate and 5-nitrodeoxyuridylate as well as the chemical and enzymic dehalogenation of 5-bromodeoxyuridine and 5-bromodeoxyuridylate. Large secondary isotope effects observed in all of these reactions provided strong evidence for the formation of 5,6-dihydropyrimidine intermediates.

INTRODUCTION

Secondary α-hydrogen isotope effects are useful tools which may aid in ascertaining whether an enzyme-catalyzed reaction or covalent interaction of an inhibitor with an enzyme involves rehybridization of a carbon atom of the ligand at or before the rate determining step of the reaction.[1,2] We have used such studies to aid our understanding of the catalytic mechanism of thymidylate synthetase, as well as the interaction of 5-fluoro-2'-deoxyuridylate (FdUMP)[3], 5-bromo-2'-deoxyuridylate (BrdUMP)[4] and 5-nitro-2'-deoxyuridylate (NO$_2$dUMP)[5] with the enzyme. An early event in the catalytic mechanism of the enzyme involves attack at the 6 position of the substrate dUMP by nucleophile of the enzyme to form a 5,6-dihydropyrimidine intermediate in which the 6-carbon is rehybridized from sp^2 to sp^3.

Here we describe the use of the α-secondary hydrogen isotope effects in the studies of the interaction of FdUMP with dTMP synthetase, as well as in the chemical and enzymic dehalogenation of 5-bromo-2'-deoxyuridine (BrdUR)[6] and 5-bromo-2'-deoxyuridylate (BrdUMP)[4] respectivety. Using the appropriate

$[2-^{14}C,6-^{3}H]$pyrimidine nucleoside/nucleotide, the presence of tritium isotope effect of 15 % or greater provides strong evidence for rehybridization at the 6-carbon and the formation of 5,6-dihydropyrimidine intermediates. Further, certain conclusion may be reached regarding the positioning of the change in rehybridization with respect to the rate determining step of the reaction.

RESULTS AND DISCUSSION

Secondary α-Hydrogen Isotope Effects in Interaction of FdUMP and CH_2- H_4folate with dTMP Synthetase[8]: A solution (3.4 ml) of the ternary complex was formed[3] using 2.25 ml of 2-fold concentrated NMM buffer[9], 2.0 nmol dTMP synthetase, 0.23 μmol d,L-CH_2-H_4folate, 30 μmol HCHO and 10.5 nmol $[2-^{14}C,6-^{3}H]$FdUMP (5.25×10^5 dpm/nmol ^{3}H; $^{3}H/^{14}C$ dpm = 4.76). Controls omitted CH_2-H_4folate. To this was added a solution (1.1 ml) containing 1.5 μmol of unlabeled FdUMP. The reaction mixture was kept at 25° under nitrogen, protected from light; triplicate aliquots were removed at intervals up to ca. 35 hr and the ternary complex isolated by adsorption on nitro-cellulose filters[3]; the aliquots filtered were progressively larger (20-500 μl) with time to obtain sufficient dpm in the isolated complex as the re-action proceeded. The triplicate samples were counted, showing standard errors of $^{3}H/^{14}C$ within 0.8 % of the mean. From these, the dissociation of the $[2-^{14}C,6-^{3}H]$FdUMP-CH_2-H_4folate-dTMP synthetase complex was shown to be first order with k_H = 0.12 hr^{-1} and the secondary isotope effect k_H/k_T was calculated[7] to be 1.23 ± 0.01 (n = 12). The large secondary isotope effect suggests that the 6-position of FdUMP is sp^3 hybridized and covalently bound to the enzyme within the isolable complex.

α-Secondary Isotope Effect in Cysteine-Promoted Dehalogenation of BrdUrd[6]: A solution (330 μl) containing 10 mM $[2-^{14}C,6-^{3}H]$BrdUrd (^{14}C, 0.614 μCi; ^{3}H, 1.89 μCi) and 0.25 M L-cysteine at pH 7.3 was incubated at 37°. Aliquots (10 μl) were removed at specified intervals, and the extent of debromination was monitored spectrophotometrically. The pseudo-first-order rate constant was 2.2×10^{-2} min^{-1}. The reactant, BrdUrd, and products, dUrd and S-[5-(2'-deoxyuridyl)]cysteine (cysdUrd), were separated by tlc as the reaction progressed, and the $^{3}H/^{14}C$ ratio of each was determined. The triti-um content of both products was enriched at initial stages of the reaction, and approached that of the initial reactant as dehalogenation progressed. Conversely, the $^{3}H/^{14}C$ ratio of the reactant decreased as the reaction pro-ceeded. From these data, the calculated k_T/k_H values for formation of dUrd

and CysdUrd are 1.187 ± 0.006 and 1.156 ± 0.007, respectively; k_T/k_H for
dehalogenation of BrdUrd is 1.174 ± 0.005 (n = 9 in each case).

α-Secondary Isotope Effect in the Thymidylate Synthetase-Catalyzed
Debromination of BrdUMP[4]: A
solution (3.5 ml) containing
50 μM[6-^{3}H,2-^{14}C]BrdUMP, (5.21
Ci/mol of ^{14}C, ^{3}H/^{14}C = 4.360),
1.1 μM dTMP synthetase, 10 mM
cysteine, 25 mM MgCl$_2$, 1 mM
EDTA and 50 mM N-methylmorpho-
line·HCl (pH 7.4) was incubated
at 37°. Aliquots (0.15 ml) were
withdrawn, dUMP and BrdUMP were
added as quenching agents and
chromatographic markers (ca. 1

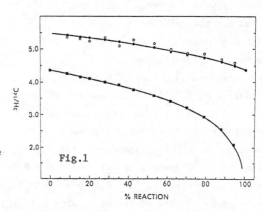

Fig.1

mM each) and the samples were immersed in ice water; this procedure was shown
to result in rapid and effective quenching of the reaction. Separations of
reactant and products were performed on Aminex A-27 as previously described[4]
using a buffer containing 0.3 M NH$_4$HCO$_3$ adjusted to pH 9.0 with NH$_4$OH; the
column temperature was 85°. Dehalogenation in a parallel reaction lacking
enzyme was negligible.

As shown in Fig. 1, the ^{3}H/^{14}C ratios of the reactant (BrdUMP ■) and the
products (dUMP ● and CysdUMP ○) change in a manner indicating a more rapid
dehalogenation of the 6-tritiated compound. The inverse secondary tritium
isotope effects (k_T/k_H) are 1.253 ± 0.003, 1.31 ± 0.03 and 1.260 ± 0.003
calculated from the ^{3}H/^{14}C ratios of dUMP, CysdUMP and BrdUMP respectively
(n = 12).

The magnitude of the inverse α-hydrogen secondary isotope effects for
the cysteine-promoted and the enzymic dehalogenation of [2-^{14}C,6-^{3}H]5-bromo-
uracil derivatives provides strong evidence for sp^2 to sp^3 rehybridization
of the 6-carbon of the heterocycle to form transient 5,6-dihydropyrimidine
intermediates.

α-Secondary Isotope Effect upon Dissociation of the [2-^{14}C,6-^{3}H]NO$_2$dUMP-
dTMP Synthetase Complex[5]: To obtain the rate of dissociation of the NO$_2$dUMP-
dTMP synthetase complex, and the secondary isotope effect, the complex was
formed utilizing 6.25 μM [2-^{14}C,6-^{3}H]NO$_2$dUMP (^{3}H dpm/^{14}C dpm = 4.049) and
2.8 μM dTMP synthetase in a total volume of 2.8 ml. After 30 min at 25°,

5.6 ml of a solution of unlabeled NO$_2$dUMP (0.8 m$\underline{M}$) in the NMM buffer[9] was added. Triplicate 200 μl aliquots were removed at specified times and the radioactive NO$_2$dUMP-dTMP synthetase complex was isolated on nitrocellulose filters[3] and dissolved in Aquasol (10 ml). A minimum of 2 x 10^5 of ^{14}C counts were collected for each sample and counting efficiencies were deter-

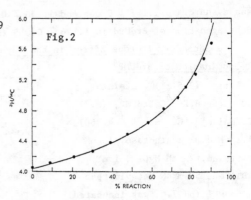

Fig.2

% REACTION

mined by the external standard ratio method; standard errors for determination of ^{3}H/^{14}C dpm's were $\underline{ca}$. 0.25 % and 0.5 %, respectively. In the present case, dissociation of [2-^{14}C,6-^{3}H]NO$_2$dUMP from complex (●) showed a large α-secondary isotope effect of k_H/k_T = 1.19 (Fig 2). In accord with the proposed interaction, this demonstrates that the 6-carbon of NO$_2$dUMP in the bound complex is sp^3 hybridized while the species released from the enzyme is sp^2 hybridized at C-6.

The above results demonstrate that secondary α-hydrogen isotope effects may be of great utility in demonstrating the existence of transient 5,6-dihydropyrimidine intermediates in both chemical and enzymic reactions of pyrimidine nucleosides and nucleotides. This method is now being applied for the study of the reaction between bisulfite and thymine.

REFERENCES

1 V. J. Shiner. Jr., "Isotope Effect in Chemical Reactions", C. J. Collins and N. S. Bowman. Ed., Van Nostrand Reinhold Co., New York, N. Y., 1970, pp 90
2 J. F. Kirsch, "Isotope Effects in Enzymology" W. W. Cleland, D. B. Northrup and M. H. O'Leary. Ed., University Park Press, Md, 1977, pp 100
3 D. V. Santi, C. S. McHenry, and H. Sommer, Biochemistry 13, 471 (1974)
4 C. Garrett, Y. Wataya and D. V. Santi, Biochemistry 18, 2798 (1979)
5 Y. Wataya, A. Matsuda and D. V. Santi, J. Biol. Chem., in press
6 Y. Wataya and D. V. Santi, J. Amer. Chem. Soc., 99, 4534 (1977)
7 L. Melander, "Isotope Effects on Reaction Rates" Ronald Press, New York, N. Y., 1960, pp 51,52
8 T. W. Bruice, C. Garrett, Y. Wataya and D. V. Santi, "Methods in Enzymology" vol 64, D. L. Purich. Ed., Academic Press, New York, N. Y., in press
9 Y. Wataya, D. V. Santi and C. Hansch, J. Med. Chem., 20, 1469 (1977)

Sensitive fluorimetry of adenine, its nucleosides and nucleotides

Masanori Yoshioka[+], Atsushi Nakamura[+], Hideaki Iizuka[+], Kazuyoshi Nishidate[+], Zenzo Tamura[+] and Tadashi Miyazaki[*]

[+]Faculty of Pharmaceutical Sciences, University of Tokyo, Hongo, Bunkyo-ku, Tokyo, and [*]Japan Spectroscopic Co., Ltd., Ishikawacho, Hachioji-city, Tokyo, Japan

ABSTRACT

We improved our fluorimetric analysis of adenine compounds by high performance liquid chromatography(HPLC). Bromoaceto-aldehyde was better than Chloro- or iodoacetoaldehyde as the reagent of fluorescent derivatization. A moderate reaction for unstable ADP and ATP was found and their fluorescent derivatives were separated by HPLC using Hitachi gel No. 3012-N. The method was applied to determine cAMP in human urines and a catechol-amine receptor system. Further, a sensitive fluorescence spectrophotometer was developed. In this micro-HPLC, several ten femtomoles of the adenine compounds were separated.

INTRODUCTION

There are many kinds of adenine containing compounds found in living bodies and synthetic chemicals. The systematic deter-mination of them is usually carried out by HPLC with an ultra violet monitor, although not so selective and sensitive.

Previously we developed a fluorimetric determination method for the adenine compounds specifically converted with chloro-acetoaldehyde to $1,N^6$-etheno adenine derivatives which were separated by HPLC (1). Later, Kuttesch et al. analysed adenosine in patients with immunodeficiency diseases in this way (2).

In this paper, we improved the method by modifying the reagent, the separation system and the detector. Further, the method was applied to measure cAMP in biological materials (3).

METHODS AND RESULTS

Bromoacetoaldehyde (4) and iodoacetoaldehyde (5) were prepared and reacted with cAMP in place of chloroacetoaldehyde. The quantity of etheno cAMP produced was determined by HPLC

described below. Bromoacetoaldehyde was found most suitable.
The yield of the reaction with bromoacetoaldehyde was 94% even
at 80°C for 15 minutes, whereas the one with chloroacetoaldehyde
was 80% at 100°C for 30 minutes.

The optimum pH in the reaction of cAMP with bromoacetoaldehyde was 5.0, where 90mM bromoacetoaldehyde was necessary
to make the yield maximum. Pyrophosphate linkages of ADP and
ATP inclined to be hydrolized at the pH. In such case, pH 7.0
was advisable to protect the unstable linkages, although 170 mM
bromoacetoaldehyde was required. A representative chromatogram
is shown in Fig. 1.

In this chromatographic system using a column of porous
polystyrene anion exchange resin Hitachi gel No. 3012-N, the
nucleotides were separated without the aid of gradient elution.
Another system based on adsorption of Hitachi gel No. 3010 was
also relevant to separation of adenine, adenosine and cAMP (1).

The method was applied to analyse biological materials,
which were cleaned up to some extent. A normal human urine
was added with deoxy-cAMP as the internal standard and passed
through a column of Dowex 50W x 4(H). The pH of the effluent
was adjusted to 5.0 and reacted with 90 mM bromoacetoaldehyde.
The reaction mixture was analysed by HPLC in Fig. 1. The mean
concentration of cAMP in six urines was 3.1 µmoles / 1 g
creatinine. Each concentration was closely corelated with the
one determined by a radioimmunoassay.

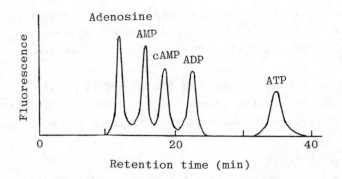

Fig. 1.   Chromatogram of 5 pmoles of authentic
          compounds reacted with bromoacetoaldehyde.

Fat cell ghosts were prepared from rats and incubated with epinephrine. The incubated suspension was passed through an alumina column to remove a large excess of ATP. The effluent was analysed in the same manner as described above. Production of cAMP was expectedly dependent on the epinephrine concentration and the incubation time.

The method was also applied to determine adenosine in synaptosomes from guinea pig cerebral cortex described elsewhere.

Further, we tried to increase the sensitivity. A fluorescence spectrophotometer FP 110 was made fit for a micropump Familic 100-N. In this HPLC, several ten femtomoles of the adenine compounds were separatively determined.

Thus, the method will be useful for basic and clinical studies.

ACKNOWLEDGMENTS

This work was supported by a grant in aid for scientific research 487145 from the Ministry of Education, Science and Culture. We are deeply grateful to Dr. N. Takai of Institute of Industrial Science, University of Tokyo for his suggestion of Hitachi gel No. 3012-N and to Mr. K. Suga of Daiichi Pure Chemicals Co., Ltd. for measuring cAMP by the radioimmunoassay.

REFERENCES

1. Yoshioka, M. and Tamura, Z.(1976) J. Chromatogr. 123, 220-224
2. Kuttesch, J. F., Schmalstieg, F. C. and Nelson, J. A.(1978) J. Liq. Chromatogr. 1, 97-109
3. Yoshioka, M., Nakamura, A., Iizuka, H., Nishidate, K., Tamura, Z. and Miyazaki, T.(1978) Abstract of the 98th Annual Meeting of Pharmaceutical Society of Japan, 533
4. Schukovskaya, L. L., Ushakov, S. N. and Galania, N. K.(1962) Izu. Akad. Nauk SSSR, Otd. Khim. Nauk, 1692-1693
5. Glinsky, Von G. (1868) Z. Chemie, 618-621

Structures of neplanocins, new antitumor antibiotics

Mitsuo Hayashi, Satoshi Yaginuma, Naoki Muto and Masatoshi Tsujino

Research Laboratories, Toyo Jozo Co. Ltd., Ohito-cho, Shizuoka 410-23, Japan

Neplanocins, novel carbocyclic analogues of purine nucleosides, are antitumor antibiotics and were isolated from the culture filtrate of *Ampullarilla regularis* A11079. Isolation of the antibiotics was performed by the successive column chromatography on ion-exchange resin and charcoal, and by partition. The antibiotics were separated into five components and named as neplanocin A(I), B(II), C(III), D(IV), and F(V), respectively. Their physico-chemical properties were summarized in Table 1.

The NMR spectrum (DMSO-d_6, 100MHz) of (I) is shown in Fig. 1. These data suggested that (I) was a cyclopentenyl adenine derivative. The vicinal diol in the sugar moiety has a *cis* configuration since (I) gave an O-iso-propylidene derivative and was cleaved rapidly with potassium metaperiodate.

Table 1. Physico-chemical Properties of Neplanocins

	(I)	(II)	(III)	(IV)	(V)
Formula	$C_{11}H_{13}N_5O_3$	$C_{11}H_{13}N_5O_4$	$C_{11}H_{13}N_5O_4$	$C_{11}H_{12}N_4O_4$	$C_{11}H_{13}N_5O_3$
M.p.(°C)	220–222 (decomp.)	269–272 (decomp.)	222–226 (decomp.)	213–216 (decomp.)	246–247 (decomp.)
$[\alpha]_D^{23}$	−157 (c=0.5,H_2O)	−3.5 (c=1.0,DMSO)	−43.6 (c=0.7,H_2O)	−145 (c=0.6,H_2O)	−6.6 (c=0.8,H_2O)
Mass	263(M^+) 136(B.P.)	279(M^+) 136(B.P.)	279(M^+) 136(B.P.)	264(M^+) 136(B.P.)	263(M^+) 136(B.P.)
$\lambda_{max}^{H_2O}$ nm (ε)	262 (15,700)	262 (15,000)	262 (15,100)	251 (12,700)	262 (15,000)
ν_{max}^{KBr} (cm$^-$)	3,320 3,200 1,650 1,640 1,600 1,570	3,400 3,300 1,695 1,640 1,605 1,565	3,400 3,240 1,680 1,630 1,600 1,565	3,400 3,260 1,680 1,585 1,550 1,510	3,300 3,200 1,650 1,640 1,600 1,570

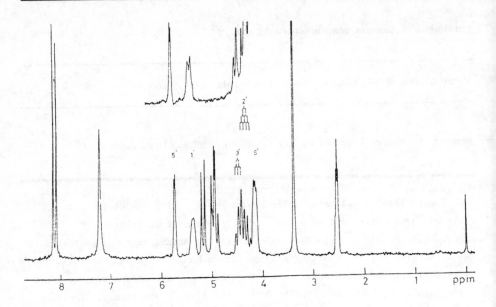

Fig. 1   NMR Spectrum of Neplanocin A (DMSO-d$_6$,100MHz)

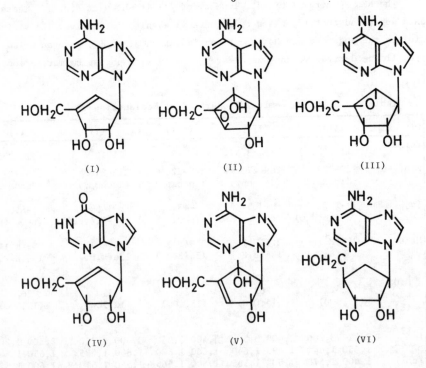

(I)   (II)   (III)

(IV)   (V)   (VI)

Fig. 2   Structures of Neplanocins and Aristeromycin

The hydrogenation of (I) with platinum oxide catalyst afforded the dihydro derivative which was identical with aristeromycin (VI)[1] in all respects. From these data described above, the structure of neplanocin A is determined as (-)-9-[trans-2,trans-3-dihydroxy-4-(hydroxymethyl)cyclopent-4-enyl]adenine (I). Further confirmation of the structure was obtained by use of X-ray analysis.

The structures of neplanocin B, C and F were also determined by the analysis of NMR spectra and other physico-chemical properties to be (II),(III) and (V), respectively. Neplanocin D was obtained by the deamination of neplanocin A.

The biological properties of neplanocins are shown in Table 2. Neplanocins exept component D have cytotoxic effect against L5178Y cells in culture. Neplanocin A, B and C have the antitumor activites in mice. Especially, neplanocin A has the most striking effect on the life prolongation in mice bearing L1210 leukemia.

Table 2. Biological Properties of Neplanocins

	(I)	(II)	(III)	(IV)	(V)
cytotoxic conc.* (µg/ml)	0.2	0.8	1.6	100	20
ILS % (mg/kg,day)**	120(5)	41(50)	30(10)	-	-
LD_{50} mouse i.p. (mg/kg)	13.7	>100	55	>100	>100

* L5178Y cells were used.
** examined against L1210 and drugs were administrated for 5 days.

ACKNOWLEDGMENTS

The authors wish to thank Dr.T.Kishi of Takeda Chemical Industries Co., Ltd. for supplying of aristeromycin sample. We express appreciation to Prof. K.Nakatsu of Kwansei Gakuin University for X-ray analysis and Prof. T.Ueda of Hokkaido University for helpful discussions and comments.

REFERENCE

1 Kusaka,T., Yamamoto,H., Shibata,M., Muroi,M., Kishi,T. and Mizuno,K., (1968) J. Antibiotics, 21, 255-263.

Neopolyoxins A, B, and C: new inhibitors of fungal cell wall chitin synthetase

Masakazu Uramoto*, Kimie Kobinata*, Kiyoshi Isono*, E.E.Jenkins**, James A.McCloskey**, Tsutomu Higashijima[+] and Tatsuo Miyazawa[+]

*The Institute of Physical and Chemical Research, Wako-shi, Saitama 351, Japan, **Departments of Medicinal Chemistry and Biochemistry, University of Utah, Salt Lake City, UT 84112, USA, and [+]Departments of Biophysics and Biochemistry, Faculty of Science, University of Tokyo, Bunkyo-ku, Tokyo 113, Japan

ABSTRACT

New inhibitors of fungal cell wall chitin synthetase were isolated and named neopolyoxins A, B, and C. The structures 1, 2, and 3 were determined on the basis of chemical and spectrometric evidence.

INTRODUCTION

A newly-isolated strain of streptomycete, *Streptomyces cacaoi* subsp. *asoensis*, was found to produce potent inhibitors of fungal cell wall chitin synthetase. Three compounds, neopolyoxins A, B, and C, were isolated and found to be nucleoside peptide antibiotics which are different from all other members of the polyoxin family.[1] The structures 1, 2, and 3 have been proposed for neopolyoxins A, B, and C, respectively.[2-4]

RESULTS

The neopolyoxins were isolated from the culture broth by cation exchange resin and charcoal column chromatographies.[2] Neopolyoxins A (1), B (2), and C (3) were separated by a Dowex 50W column buffered with pyridine-acetic or formic acid (pH 3.4-5.0) and by cellulose column chromatography (butanol-acetic acid -H_2O).

Enzymatic hydrolysis of these three antibiotics yielded nucleosides (4, 5, 6, respectively) and a common amino acid (7). A nucleoside from neopolyoxin C (3) was identical with uracil polyoxin C (6), which is a basic nucleoside skeleton of the polyoxin family. Compound (6) was treated with bromine followed by sodium bicarbonate yielded 2-oxo-4-imidazoline-4-carboxylic acid nucleoside (5) which was identical with a nucleoside obtained from neopolyoxin B (2). A nucleoside (4)[5] from neopolyoxin A (1) was oxidized with silver oxide to give nucleoside (5). Since the absolute configuration of uracil polyoxin C (6) is firmly established[1], this chemical interconversion is an unambiguous proof for the absolute structures of 4 and 5.

A common side chain amino acid (7) of neopolyoxins A, B, and C was isolated. Spectrometric data (UV, ^{1}H and ^{13}C NMR, mass spectrum of a trimethylsilyl derivative) supported the structure, 2-amino-4-hydroxy-4-(5-hydroxy-2-pyridyl)-3-methylbutyric acid. Absolute configuration (2S, 3S, 4R) of 7 was assigned by NOE enhancements of γ-lactone diacetate (8) and CD of the hydrogenated amino acid.

Chemical transformation ($\underset{\sim}{6} \rightarrow \underset{\sim}{5}$) originally discovered by Fox et al[6] may reflect a biosynthetic event in the cell.

REFERENCES AND NOTES

1. Isono,K., Asahi,K., and Suzuki,S. (1969)J.Am.Chem.Soc.91, 7490-7505.
2. Kobinata,K., Uramoto,M., Nishii,M., Kusakabe,H., Nakamura,G., and Isono,K. Agric.Biol.Chem., submitted.
3. Uramoto,M., Kobinata,K., Isono,K., Jenkins,E.E., and McCloskey,J.A. Tetrahedron Lett., submitted.
4. Uramoto,M., Kobinata,K., Isono,K., Higashijima,T., and Miyazawa,T. Tetrahedron Lett., submitted.
5. This nucleoside was identical with the nucleoside obtained from polyoxin N.[7] Therefore, the structure of polyoxin N must be revised as follows:[8]

6. Otter,B.A., Falco,E.A., and Fox,J.J. (1969)J.Org.Chem.34, 2636-2642.
7. Uramoto,M., Uzawa,J., Suzuki,S., Isono,K., Liehr,J.G., and McCloskey,J.A. (1978)Nucleic Acids Res.,Special Publication, 5,s327-s330.
8. Uramoto,M., Isono,K., Liehr,J.G., and McCloskey,J.A. Tetrahedron Lett., submitted.

Structure of amipurimycin, a new nucleoside antibiotic produced by Streptomyces novoguineensis

Toshio Goto, Yoshiaki Toya and Tadao Kondo

Department of Agricultural Chemistry, Nagoya University, Chikusa, Nagoya 464, Japan

ABSTRACT

Structure elucidation of a new 2-aminopurine nucleoside antibiotic amipurimycin has been carried out. It contains 2-aminopurine, cis-2-aminocyclopentane-1-carboxylic acid and a sugar moiety. A structure will be proposed for the antibiotic.

INTRODUCTION

Harada and Kishi[1] isolated from Streptomyces novoguineensis antibiotic amipurimycin (1) (APM) [$C_{20}H_{27-31}N_7O_8$, mp 215°C (dec), pKa' 3.7 and 9.1, positive ninhydrin test], which is active against Pyricularia oryzae. ^{13}C nmr and uv (λ_{max} 218, 243 and 305 nm) spectra suggested the presence of 2-aminopurine base (2). We have carried out structure determination of this antibiotic.

RESULTS AND DISCUSSION

FD mass spectrum showed its mol. formula to be $C_{20}H_{29}N_7O_8$. Its pKa, ninhydrin test, ir (1600 cm^{-1} br.) and ^{13}C nmr (176.26, 175.84) suggested the presence of an amino and a carboxylic acid group in a zwitterionic form. Acid hydrolysis gave an amino acid, whose structure was deduced as cis-2-aminocyclopentane-1-carboxylic acid (3) by comparison of synthetic cis-[2] and trans-amino acid.[3]

(2)   (3)

Treatment of APM (1) with HCl in methanol afforded APM methyl ester hydrochloride (4), which was further converted with acetic anhydride and pyridine to hexaacetyl APM methyl ester (5). Analysis of nmr spectra of APM (1) and hexaacetyl APM methyl ester (5) suggested the following partial formulae (nmr data are for the acetate).

(Chem. shifts δppm; Coupling const.in Hz)

Mild acetylation of APM methyl ester (4) with p-nitrophenyl acetate and pyridine gave N-acetyl APM methyl ester (6), which was treated with 2,2-dimethoxypropane in the presence of camphorsulfonic acid in acetone to afford monoacetonide I. By a longer reaction time the acetonide I was partially converted to monoacetonide II.

A structure will be proposed for amipurimycin (1) by comparison of physical and spectral data of these derivatives.

Acknowledgement

We thank Takeda Chemical Industries, Ltd., Central Research Division, for providing amipurimycin.

REFERENCES
(1) Harada, S. and Kishi, T. (1977) J. Antibiotics 30, 11-16
(2) Nativ, E. and Roua, R. (1972) Israel J. Chem. 10, 55
(3) Plieninger, H. and Schneider, K. (1959) Chem. Ber. 92, 1594

Template-directed synthesis of oligoadenylate. Template effect of oligouridylates and catalytic activity of Pb^{2+} ion

Hiroaki Sawai

Faculty of Pharmaceutical Sciences, University of Tokyo, Hongo, Bunkyo-ku, Tokyo 113, Japan

ABSTRACT

Template-directed condensation of adenosine-5'-phosphorimi-dazolide was conducted in the presence of oligouridylate template. Oligouridylates with more than eight chain units can serve as a template and facilitate oligoadenylate formation. Internucleotide linkage of the oligoadenylate obtained by this reaction was mainly 2'-5'. Addition of Pb^{2+} ion catalyst to this reaction system promoted the formation of long oligoadenylates. The template with Pb^{2+} ion catalyst preferentially gave 3'-5' linked oligoadenylates.

INTRODUCTION

Poly U and adenylic acid form triple helix according to Watson-Crick base pairing rule. Chemical polymerization of ade-nylic acid is promoted by poly U template.[1] In another experi-ment, we have shown that Pb^{2+} ion facilitates the condensation of adenosine-5'-phosphorimidazolide (ImpA) even in the absence of poly U template.[2] The minimum length of nucleotide chain re-quired to serve as a template for the template-directed conden-sation and catalytic effect of metal ion on the reaction has been a matter of speculation. Here we describe the condensation of ImpA on various oligo U templates. Further, we show the cat-alytic effect of Pb^{2+} ion on template-directed condensation of ImpA on oligo U.

EXPERIMENTAL

ImpA was prepared from adenylic acid and imidazole.[3] Oli-gouridylates ((pU)$_n$ n=2-14) were prepared by partial hydrolysis of poly U.[4] Condensation of ImpA (0.025M) was carried out in the presence of oligo U (0.05M), MgCl$_2$ (0.075M) and NaCl (0.2M)

at pH 7.5 and 0°C for 16 days. When Pb^{2+} was used as a catalyst, $Pb(NO_3)_2$ (0.0125M) was added to the reaction mixture, and $Mg(NO_3)_2$ and $NaNO_3$ were used instead of $MgCl_2$ and NaCl. The products were separated by paper chromatography.

RESULTS AND DISCUSSION

Table 1 shows some yield data of the products obtained from ImpA in the presence of oligo U template. Oligo U with chain

Table 1. Condensation of ImpA on Oligo U Template

Template	Yield (%)					
	ImpA	pA	$(pA)_2$*	$(pA)_3$	$(pA)_4$	$(pA)_5$
—	70.3	24.5	5.0	0.1		
$(pU)_6$	52.2	39.3	7.9	0.6		
$(pU)_8$	40.1	39.9	16.3	2.6	0.1	
$(pU)_{12}$	34.4	31.8	24.2	5.9	2.7	0.8
Poly U	13.3	22.6	36.7	14.1	6.6	5.7

* ImpApA is included.

length more than eight can serve as a template for the condensation of ImpA. The yield of the oligoadenylates increased with increasing chain length of the oligo U template. No template activity was observed when oligo U below a hexamer was used. 2'-5' Linked oligoadenylates were preferentially formed in the reaction (93-97%).

Table 2 shows the yield data of Pb^{2+} ion-catalyzed condensation of ImpA on oligo U template. Oligo U with chain length

Table 2. Condensation of ImpA in the Presence of Oligo U Template and Pb^{2+} Ion Catalyst. (4 days)

Template	Yield (%)					
	ImpA	pA	$(pA)_2$*	$(pA)_3$	$(pA)_4$	$(pA)_5$†
—	6.0	21.5	43.3	12.0	8.2	8.9
$(pU)_6$	5.0	25.7	27.5	10.1	9.7	9.7
$(pU)_8$	3.2	20.2	21.2	12.5	12.4	16.9
$(pU)_{12}$	4.6	18.3	21.8	15.4	13.3	22.5
Poly U	2.7	16.0	20.7	18.8	15.5	26.3

* ImpApA is included.
† Oligoadenylates more than a pentamer are included.

more than eight units promoted the formation of long oligoadenylates and decreased the yield of diadenylate. Internucleotide linkage of diadenylates was mainly 2'-5' (83-88%) in the reaction where oligo U up to a hexamer was used and in the control reaction. However, higher oligo U more than an octamer increased the ratio of 3'-5' linkage (40-75%) with increasing chain length of oligo U. Poly U template with Pb^{2+} ion catalyst gave 3'-5' linked oligoadenylate preferentially.[5] Template effect of oligo U and Pb^{2+} ion catalyst controls the selectivity of internucleotide linkage.

Results of the two series of reactions show that the minimum length required for the template activity is as short as eight.

REFERENCES

1. Orgel, L. E. and Lohrmann, R. (1974) Accounts Chem. Res. 7, 368.
2. Sawai, H. (1976) J. Am. Chem. Soc. 98, 7037.
3. Lohrmann, R. and Orgel, L. E. (1978) Tetrahedron 34, 853.
4. Heppel, L. A. (1966) Procedures in Nucleic Acid Research, ed. by G. L. Cantoni and D. R. Davies, p. 31, Harper and Row Pub., New York.
5. Sleeper, H. L., Lohrmann, R., Orgel, L. E. (1979) J. Mol. Evol. 13, 203.

Synthesis of uridine oligonucleotide by the reaction of unprotected uridine with tri- (imidazolyl-(1)) phosphine

Takeo Shimizdu, Kazushige Yamana, Akira Murakami and Kikumi Nakamichi

Department of Hydrocarbon Chemistry, Faculty of Engineering, Kyoto University, Kyoto 606, Japan

ABSTRACT

Uridine oligonucleotide was synthesized by the reaction of unprotected uridine with tri-(imidazolyl-(1))phosphine and the successive oxidation of the resulting cyclic phosphite with iodine and water. The uridine oligonucleotide obtained from this reaction contained both 3'-5'linkage and 2'-5'linkage. The type of the phosphodiester linkage was resulted at the oxidative ring-opening reaction, and it was controlled by poly-nucleotides and various divalent metal cations.

INTRODUCTION

Various applications of phosphorus compounds in nucleotide syntheses have been reported[1]. Recently, oligonucleotide synthesis via phosphite intermediate has been successfully achieved[2] and adapted to polymer supported oligonucleotide synthesis[3]. However, tri-(imidazolyl-(1))phosphine has not been used for the phosphorylation of nucleoside because of the lack of its stability[4].

We have first tried to adapt tri-(imidazolyl-(1))phosphine to uridine oligonucleotide synthesis. The synthetic procedure involves the following two step process; (1) the reaction of un-protected uridine with tri-(imidazolyl-(1))phosphine(within 60 min). (2) the in $situ$ oxidation of the resulting cyclic phos-phite with iodine and water(10 min). The uridine oligonucleo-tide obtained from this reaction contains both 3'-5'linkage and 2'-5'linkage. This report gives the outline of uridine oligonucleotide synthesis by the reaction of unprotected uridine with tri-(imidazolyl-(1))phosphine and effects of polynucleotides and various divalent metal cations on the oxidative ring-opening reaction at which the type of the phosphodiester linkage is

Nucleic Acids Research

resulted.

EXPERIMENTAL

Tri-(imidazolyl-(1))phosphine was prepared by the reaction
of phosphorus trichloride with imidazole(1:6,mol/mol) in anhydrous THF at 0°C under nitrogen for 20 min.

The reaction of uridine with tri-(imidazolyl-(1))phosphine
was carried out in pyridine-THF at -78°C. After 60 min, oxi-
dations with iodine and water in the presence or absence of
polynucleotides and various divalent metal cations[5] were done at
0°C for 10 min. The products were separated on a DEAE-cellulose
column chromatography. The phosphodiester linkage was investigated by snake venom phosphodiesterase, spleen phosphodiesterase,
and alkaline hydrolysis of the products.

RESULTS AND DISCUSSION

The analytical results of the reaction products by means of
high pressure liquid chromatography, paper chromatography, and
paper electrophoresis showed that the amount of oligonucleotide
material formed did not significantly increase after 60 min.
It is noteworthy that the polymerization reaction was almost
completed within 60 min under the present condition. The
products were separated on a DEAE-cellulose column chromatography. Only the linear uridine oligonucleotides((Up)$_n$ and
(Up)$_n$U) up to the hexanucleotides were obtained(Yield,85.5%).
In the products, however, Up and Up! were not found.

The phosphodiester linkage in the oligonucleotides was
investigated by snake venom phosphodiesterase, spleen phospho-

5' terminus = -OH

I₂+H₂O → Up , Up! not found

Nucleic Acids Research

resulted.

EXPERIMENTAL

Tri-(imidazolyl-(1))phosphine was prepared by the reaction
of phosphorus trichloride with imidazole(1:6,mol/mol) in anhydrous THF at 0°C under nitrogen for 20 min.

The reaction of uridine with tri-(imidazolyl-(1))phosphine
was carried out in pyridine-THF at -78°C. After 60 min, oxi-
dations with iodine and water in the presence or absence of
polynucleotides and various divalent metal cations[5] were done at
0°C for 10 min. The products were separated on a DEAE-cellulose
column chromatography. The phosphodiester linkage was investigated by snake venom phosphodiesterase, spleen phosphodiesterase,
and alkaline hydrolysis of the products.

RESULTS AND DISCUSSION

The analytical results of the reaction products by means of
high pressure liquid chromatography, paper chromatography, and
paper electrophoresis showed that the amount of oligonucleotide
material formed did not significantly increase after 60 min.
It is noteworthy that the polymerization reaction was almost
completed within 60 min under the present condition. The
products were separated on a DEAE-cellulose column chromatography. Only the linear uridine oligonucleotides((Up)$_n$ and
(Up)$_n$U) up to the hexanucleotides were obtained(Yield,85.5%).
In the products, however, Up and Up! were not found.

The phosphodiester linkage in the oligonucleotides was
investigated by snake venom phosphodiesterase, spleen phospho-

s82

diesterase, and alkaline degradations.   The results of these
degradations show that the produced uridine oligonucleotides
contain both 3'-5'linkage and 2'-5'linkage but no 5'-5'linkage
and 3'-3'linkage.   Consequently, it is considered that tri-
(imidazolyl-(1))phosphine does not attack to 5'-OH of uridine in
the first phosphorylation step and the polymerization reaction
proceeds *via* uridine 2',3'-cyclic phosphorimidazole 2 which is
formed by the selective attack of tri-(imidazolyl-(1))phosphine
to 2'-OH and 3'-OH of uridine.   This intermediate 2 is considered to be highly reactive and reacts rapidly with 1 or 2 at
5'-OH soon after the formation because of no detection of Up or
Up! in the products.

     Uridine oligonucleotides 4 were easily obtained by the *in
situ* oxidation of the oligomer 3 with iodine and water.   This
process involves the oxidation of cyclic phosphite triester and
the ring-opening reaction of the resulting cyclic phosphate.
The type of the phosphodiester linkage is resulted from the
cleavage of either 2'-O-P or 3'-O-P.   Of UpU produced in the
absence of the additive material, the ratio of 3'-5'linkage:
2'-5'linkage was 1:2(mol/mol).

     Effects of polynucleotides and various divalent metal

Table 1.   The phosphodiester linkage in UpU formed under
the various conditions of the oxidative ring-opening
reaction in the presence of polynucleotides and divalent
metal cations

	3'-5'linkage/%	2'-5'linkage/%
none	32	68
PolyA	52	48
PolyU	12	88
$MnCl_2$	45	55
$CaCl_2$	27	73
$MgCl_2$	35	65
$ZnCl_2$	25	75
$NiCl_2$	29	71
$CuCl_2$	28	72
$Pb(NO_3)_2$	28	72
$Co(NO_3)_2$	43	57

cations on the oxidative ring-opening reaction of the oligomer
3 were investigated.   The results were shown in Table 1.   The
3'-5'phosphodiester linkage in UpU was increased in the presence
of PolyA.   On the contrary, the 3'-5'linkage in UpU was
decreased to 12% in the presence of PolyU.   This fact implies
a specific interaction between polynucleotides and the oligomer
3.   In the case of divalent metal cations, Mn^{++} and Co^{++} of
which cordination number is six affected the oxidative ring-
opening reaction of the oligomer 3, and gave much 3'-5'linkage
in UpU.

REFERENCES AND NOTES

1. Korby,N.S., Kenner,G.W., and Todd,A.R., *J.Chem.Soc.*, 3669
   (1952).   Kenner,G.W., Todd,A.R., and Weymouth,F.J., *ibid.*,
   3675(1952).   Schofield,J.A. and Todd,A.R., *ibid.*, 2316
   (1961).   Holy,A. and Sorm,F., *Collect.Czech.Chem.Commun.*,
   31, 1544(1966).   Holy,A. and Sorm,F., *ibid.*, 31, 1562
   (1966).   Honjo,M., Marumoto,R., Kusashio,K., and Yoshikawa,
   Y., *Tetrahedron Lett.* 3851(1966).   Yoshikawa,M., Sakuraba,
   M., and Kusashio.K., *Bull.Chem.Soc.Jpn.*, 43, 456(1970).
   Sekine,M., Mori,H., and Hata,T., *Tetrahedron Lett.*, 1145
   (1979).
2. Letsinger,R.L. and Lunsford,W.B., *J.Amer.Chem.Soc.*, 98,
   3655(1976).
3. Matteucci,M.D. and Caruthers,M.H., *Tetrahedron Lett.*, 719
   (1980).
4. Birkofer,L. and Ritter,A., *Angew.Chem.*, 73, 134(1961).
   Staab,H.A., *Angew.Chem.Internat.Edit.*, 1, 351(1962).
5. Polynucleotides were used two fold excess of uracil moiety.
   Divalent metal cations were used in equimolar amount to the
   phosphine.
6. A part of this work was reported by Shimidzu,T., Yamana,K.,
   Murakami,A., and Nakamichi,K., *Tetrahedron Lett.*, in press.

A new method for the synthesis of dinucleoside polyphosphates via stannyl-ester intermediates

Takashi Kamimura, Shinkichi Honda, Kazunori Terada, Yumi Osaki, Mitsuo Sekine and Tsujiaki Hata*

Department of Life Chemistry, Tokyo Institute of Technology, Nagatsuta, Midoriku, Yokohama 227, Japan

ABSTRACT

Tri-n-butylstannyl esters of guanylic acid and related compounds were found to be soluble in pyridine and useful as synthetic key-intermediates for polyphosphate bond formation.

Considerable attention has recently been paid to the chemical synthesis of biologically active genes such as double-strand DNAs and transfer-RNAs. On the other hand, the so-called "cap" structure, represented as $m^7G^{5'}pppX(m)pYpZ...$, has been found commonly at the 5'-terminus of eukaryotic mRNAs, viral mRNAs, heterogeneous nuclear RNAs, and several species of low molecular weight nuclear RNAs[1]. In spite of the attractive structure, significant efforts have not been made for the chemical synthesis of such mRNAs up to date, since the "cap" structure was so unstable that synthetic reactions and separation of products should be performed under limited conditions. We previously studied the chemical synthesis of the 5'-terminal part of the mRNA from CPV where $m^7G^{5'}pppG$ or $G^{5'}pppG$ was synthesized by the reaction of ArSppG or $ArSppm^7G$ with pG or pm^7G in the presence of iodine[2]. However, this method involves the essential problem that the yield of α,γ-dinucleoside triphosphates is unsatisfactory owing to the extremely poor solubility of guanylic acid derivatives in organic solvents.

In this paper, we wish to report the utility of stannylated guanylic acid and its derivatives as synthetic intermediates which will be applicable to the synthesis of unsymmetrical α,γ-dinucleoside triphosphates.

In the course of our study on acyl phosphates[3], it was found that stannyl phosphates were more soluble in organic solvents than the corresponding unstannylated esters. For example, pyridinium or other ammonium salts of pG become a gel in dry pyridine, whereas the corresponding bis(tri-n-butyl-stannyl) derivatives are easily dissolved in the solvent.

The stannylation of pG and pm^7G could be readily performed by use of bis(tri-n-butyltin) oxide or by Dowex 50W X8 (Bu_3Sn-form) resin. The bis(tri-n-butyl)stannyl ester of pG was found to be quite easily dissolved in organic solvents and suffi-ciently reactive in chemical transformations into other deriva-tives. The "capping" reagent ArSppNu was also prepared via the corresponding stannyl ester according to the following Scheme.

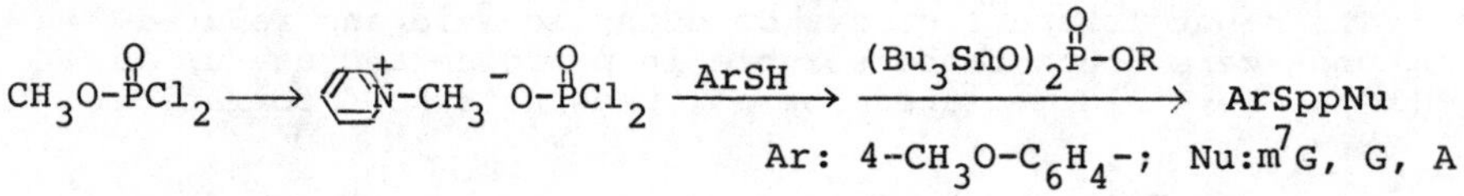

$$CH_3O-\overset{O}{\overset{\parallel}{P}}Cl_2 \longrightarrow \langle \rangle \overset{+}{N}-CH_3 \;\; {}^-O-\overset{O}{\overset{\parallel}{P}}Cl_2 \xrightarrow{ArSH} \xrightarrow{(Bu_3SnO)_2\overset{O}{\overset{\parallel}{P}}-OR} ArSppNu$$

Ar: $4-CH_3O-C_6H_4-$; Nu: m^7G, G, A

Now, it was found that tri-n-butylstannyl i-propyl S-phenyl phosphorothioate underwent smooth reaction with bis(tri-n-butyl-stannyl) thymidine 5'-phosphate in the presence of iodine to give an unsymmetrical pyrophosphate, i-PrppT, in good yield. This facile reaction should be emphasized since phosphorothio-ates of triester-type are known not to be activated by iodine under the usual conditions. In a simmilar manner, i-PrppG was obtained where the reaction proceeded always homogeneously.

Further application of the present reaction to the synthesis of α,γ-dinucleoside triphosphates is now in progress and the capping reaction with oligoribonucleotides will be also discussed.

REFERNCES
1 Rottman, F. M. (1978) International Review of Biochemistry, Biochemistry of Nucleic Acids II, Vol. 17, pp.45-73.
2 Yamaguchi, K., Nakagawa, I., Hata, T., Shimotohno, K., Shimotohno, K., Hiruta, M., and Miura, K. (1976) Nucleic Acids Synposium Series No. 2, s 151.
3 Nakagawa, I., Konya, S, Ohtani, S., and Hata, T. (1980) Synthesis, in the press.
4 Yamaguchi, K., Kamimura, T., and Hata, T. (1980) J. Am. Chem. Soc., in the press.

Symposium Series No.8 1980

Nucleic Acids Research

Synthesis of the 3'- and 5'-reiterated terminal sequences of Rous sarcoma virus 35S RNA

Hiroshi Takaku, Tadaaki Nomoto and Kazuo Kamaike

Laboratory of Organic Chemistry, Chiba Institute of Technology, Narashino, Chiba 275, Japan

The structure of Rous sarcoma virus (RSV) 35S RNA has recently been determined at the 3'-[1] and 5'- ends[2] by two groups. Twenty one bases at the extreme 5' end has been found to be identical to twenty one bases adjacent to the poly(A) terminus at the 3' end of the same molecule (Fig. 1). The existence of these reiterated terminal sequences suggests mechanisms by which the growing DNA copy can jump from the 5' end to a 3' end of the template and become circular proviral DNA.[3]

Fig. 1.

RSV 35S RNA

m^7GpppG^{m}CCAUUUUACCAUUCACCACA......GCCAUUUUACCAUUCACCACApoly(A)

In the present paper, we describe synthesis of twenty one nucleotides of the 3'- and 5'-reitrated terminal sequences of RSV 35S RNA by the phosphotriester approach.

Syntheis of the heptamer, CACCACA (12) using 5'-O-dimethoxytrityl 2'-O-tetrahydropyranylnucleoside 3'-(4-chloro-pheny, 5-chloro-8-quinolyl) phoshates (1).

The present approach to the synthesis of heptanucleotide (12) is summarised in Fig. 2.

The fully protected monoribonucleotides (1) as key inter-mediates for the ribooligonucleotides synthesis by the modified triester method were prepared by the following procedure: To a THF solution of 4-chlorophenyl phosphorodichloridate was added a THF of 5-chloro-8-hydroxyquinoline[4] and triethylamine,

Fig 2

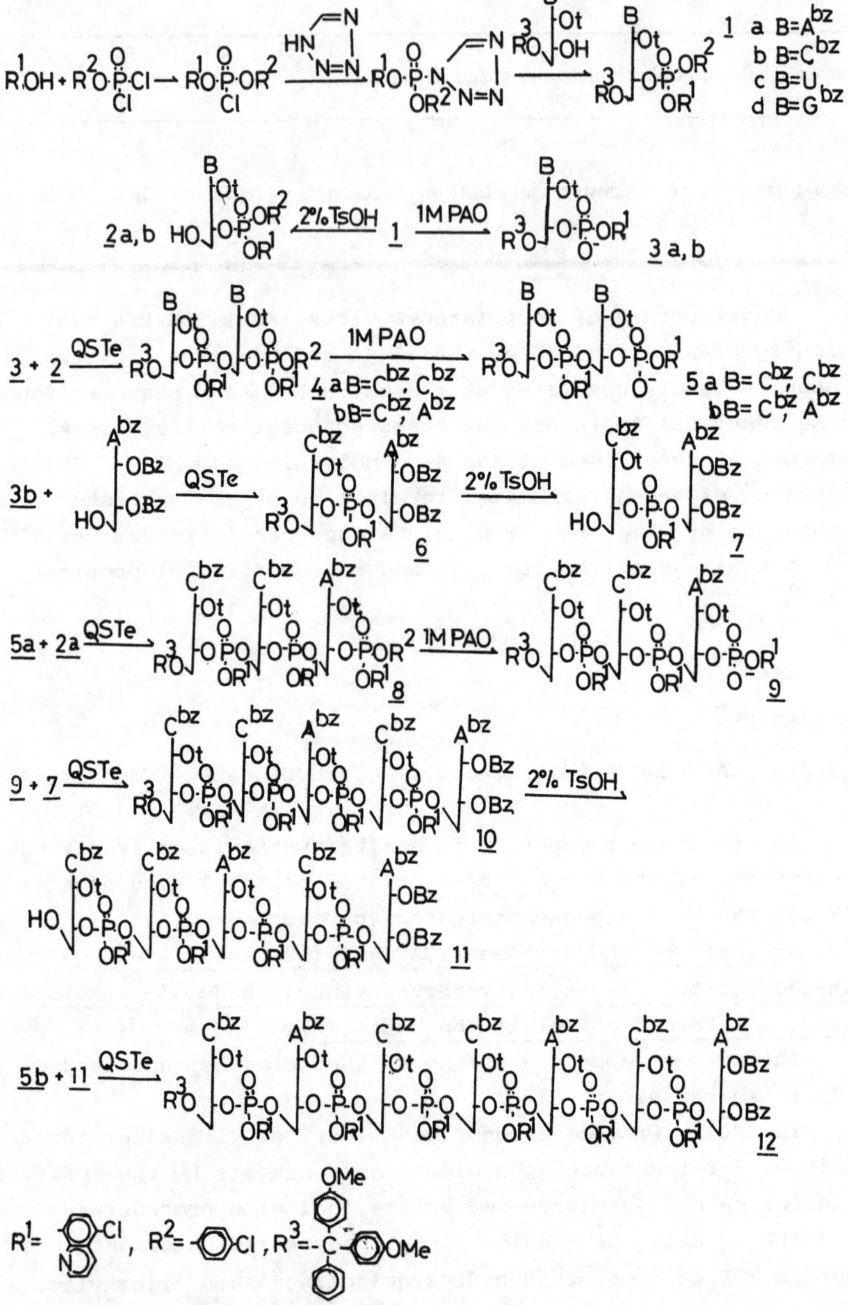

and the mixture was stirred for 45 min.   After completion of
the reaction, the reaction mixture was treated with tetrazole
and triethylamine for 10 min.   The precipitated triethylammonium
hydrochloride was removed by filtration.   To this filtrate was
added 5'-O-dimethoxytrityl 2'-O-tetranydropyranylnucleoside
and the mixture was kept for 30 min.   After usual work-up, the
corresponding fully protected monoribonucleotides (1a-d) were
isolated in 91, 92, 96, an 82% yields, respectively, after
separation by silica gel column chromatography.

The fully protected monoribonucleotides (1) were treated
with 2% p-toluenesulphonic acid solution[4] to give 2.   The 5'-
hydroxyl nucleotides (2) were key intermediates as 3'-terminal
units in the synthesis of terminally diesterified blocks.
On the other hand, 1 could be converted to the phosphodiesters
(3) by removing the 4-chlorophenyl group with 1M N^1,N^1,N^3,N^3-
tetramethylguanidium salt of 2-pyridinaldoxime[5] in order to
elongate the chain in the 3' direction.   For the synthesis of
dinucleotides (4), 2 was condensed with 3 using 8-quinoline-
sulphonyltetrazolide (QSTe)[6] as a powerful coupling agent.

In a similar manner, the fully protected trimer (8),
pentamer (10), and heptamer (12) were isolated (72-85%) by silica
gel column chromatography.

REFERENCES

1. Schwartz,D.E. Zamecnik,P.C. and Weith,H.L. (1977) Proc.Natl.
   Acad.Sci.USA, 74,994-998.
2. Haseltine,W.A. Maxam,A.M. and Gilbert,W. (1977)Proc.Natl.
   Acad.Sci.USA, 74,989-993.
3. Taylor,J.M. (1977) Biochim.Biophys.Acta, 473,57-71.
4. Takaku,H. Nomoto,T. Sakamoto,Y and Hata,T (1979) Chem.Lett.,
   1225-1228; Takaku,H Yamaguchi,R Nomoto,T and Hata,T (1979)
   Tetrahedron Lett., 3857-3860.
5. Reese,C.B. Titmas,R.C. and Yau,L. (1978) Tetrahedron Lett.,
   2727-2730.
6. Takaku,H Yoshida,M and Hata,T. Nucleic Acids Res.Spec.Pub.,
   6,s181-182.

The synthesis and properties of some 5-substituted uracil derivatives

R.T.Walker[*], A.S.Jones[*], E.De Clercq[+], J.Descamps[+], H.S.Allaudeen[†] and J.W.Kozarich[†]

*Chemistry Department, Birmingham University, Birmingham B15 2TT, UK, +Rega Instituut, Katholieke Universiteit Leuven, B-3000 Leuven, Belgium, and †Pharmacology Department, Yale University School of Medicine, New Haven, CT 06510, USA

ABSTRACT

The chemical syntheses of some 5-substituted uracil derivatives, in particular 5-vinyl-2'-deoxyuridine, 5-ethynyl-2'-deoxyuridine and 5-(2-bromovinyl)-2'-deoxy-uridine are reviewed and their potential as radiation sensitizing agents, anti-cancer agents and antiviral agents is discussed. 5-Ethynyl-2'-deoxyuridine is not incorporated into DNA; is a thymidylate synthetase inhibitor and has a possible use as an anti-cancer drug. 5-Vinyl-2'-deoxyuridine can replace thymidine residues in DNA of phage T3; does not cause the organism to be significantly more sensitive to γ-radiation but its presence in DNA causes the organism to lose viability, possibly through chemical cross-linking reactions of the vinyl group. 5-(2-Bromovinyl)-2'-deoxyuridine is the most specific and potent antiherpes compound yet known. Its mode of action and its affects on herpes virus in vitro and in vivo with animal models and clinical observations are described.

Introduction and attempts to incorporate 5-substituted uracils into DNA

For some years we have been concerned with the synthesis of 5-substituted uracil derivatives, initially as potential radiation-sensitizing compounds but more recently as more conventional anti-cancer and antiviral agents.[1-28] Our original objectives were the syntheses of 5-vinyluracil[1] and 5-ethynyluracil[7] and these were achieved although many other groups reported syntheses of these compounds around the same time.[29-33] Subsequently we have synthesized the deoxynucleosides (and ribonucleosides) of these bases using standard nucleoside condensation conditions and some of these derivatives have been reported by us[21-27] and by others[34-37] to have potential use as anti-herpes virus derivatives and others to show a toxicity to cells in tissue culture which might make them suitable as anti-cancer drugs.[28,37] In order to be capable of acting as radiation-sensitizing agents, we expected that these thymine or thymidine analogues would need to be incorporated into DNA such that local ionizing radiation would then produce compounds which would cause cell death.

Thus over a period of some years, we have attempted the incorporation of the

$$R = -CH=CH_2 \quad : \text{5-vinyl-dU}$$

$$-C \equiv CH \quad : \text{5-ethynyl-dU}$$

bases and deoxynucleosides of the 5-vinyl- and 5-ethynyluracil into the DNA of various organisms – a thymine requiring mutant of E. coli, a mycoplasma species (these organisms have no cell wall and DNA with a high thymine content) and a virus, T3 phage. The results are summarized below. It has not been possible to incorporate 5-ethynyluracil or its deoxynucleoside into DNA. We now have evidence that 5-ethynyl-2'-deoxyuridine 5'-phosphate is an inhibitor of thymidylate synthetase and this would provide a satisfactory explanation for these results and for the toxicity of these analogues.

5-Vinyluracil can however be incorporated into DNA to replace thymine residues. This incorporation is usually accompanied by appreciable cell death and this is most clearly seen in the case of phage T3,[15] where initially the phage particles containing the analogue are viable but they very quickly lose viability on standing. The deoxynucleoside 5'-phosphate of 5-vinyluracil and 5-hydroxymethyluracil are not thymidylate synthetase inhibitors[28] and the toxicity of these compounds seems to be dependent upon their incorporation into DNA followed by a chemical cross-linking reaction.[15,34]

Thus 5-ethynyluracil seems to have no potential as a radiation-sensitizing agent and although 5-vinyluracil has been incorporated into DNA of E. coli, a mycoplasma and T3 phage, this incorporation alone seems to result in cell death and the apparent

Incorporation results

Analogue	E. coli T⁻		Mycoplasma		Phage T3	
	ID_{50}	Inc.	ID_{50}	Inc.	ID_{50}	Inc.
5-Bromouracil	10	20 (2.5 µM)	>1000	18	-	-
5-Bromo-2'-deoxyuridine	2.5	24 (2.5 µM)	>1000	33	>100	100
5-Vinyluracil	35	10	>2500	24 (1 mM)	>100	32
5-Vinyl-2'-deoxyuridine	-	-	>500	4	50	0
5-Ethynyluracil	1.2	0	250	0	>50	0
5-Ethynyl-2'-deoxyuridine	-	-	250	0	<1	-

ID_{50}, concentration (µM) required to reduce viability by 50%, incorporation (Inc.) of analogue into DNA is expressed as % thymidine replaced. Concentration of analogue in the growth medium was 50 µM unless otherwise indicated by figures in parentheses.

radiation sensitivity conferred upon Mycoplasma because of incorporation of the analogue into its DNA could well have some other explanation.

Synthesis and biological properties of some antiviral nucleosides

So far, we have only considered 5-substituted uracil derivatives which have been relatively toxic. During the search for a viable synthesis of 5-ethynyluracil, we obtained E-5-(2-bromovinyl)uracil.[6] The deoxynucleoside of this base has subsequently been shown to be the most selective and potent anti-herpes virus agent yet reported.[22] The original preparation of this deoxynucleoside was rather lengthy with an overall yield

Y = OH , X = Cl : E-5-(2-chlorovinyl)-2'-deoxyuridine (CVDU)
Y = OH , X = Br : E-5-(2-bromovinyl)-2'-deoxyuridine (BVDU)
Y = OH , X = I : E-5-(2-iodovinyl)-2'-deoxyuridine (IVDU)
Y = NH₂, X = Br : E-5-(2-bromovinyl)-2'-deoxycytidine (BVDC)
Y = NH₂, X = I : E-5-(2-iodovinyl)-2'-deoxycytidine (IVDC)

of <10% and more recently the adaptation of a method for the arylation of olefins first used in the nucleoside field by Bergstrom and co-workers,[38-40] has resulted in the synthesis of the five compounds listed.[12] Further work on the synthesis of other potential antiviral compounds in this area is at present in progress. The relative potency and selectivity of these derivatives as anti-herpes agents in primary rabbit kidney cell cultures is given below. The corresponding figures for 5-iodo-2'-deoxyuridine (IDU) the compound currently in clinical use and for 9-(2-hydroxyethoxymethyl)guanine (acycloguanosine, Acyclovir, ACG)[41] and for 2'-fluoro-5-iodoaracytosine (FIAC)[42] are also given.

Compound	Antiviral activity (A)	Antimetabolic activity (B)	Selectivity index A/B
CVDU	0.02	>200	>10000
BVDU	0.007	70	10000
IVDU	0.01	70	7000
BVDC	0.07	>200	>3000
IVDC	0.1	>200	>2000
ACG	0.06	7	117
FIAC	0.02	40	2000
IDU	0.2	1.2	6

A = concentration (μg/ml) of compound required to inhibit cytopathogenicity of HSV-1 by 50%

B = concentration (μg/ml) of compound required to inhibit the incorporation of 2'-deoxyuridine into cellular DNA by 50%

Most of the subsequent biological, pharmacological and clinical work has been done with BVDU and the most recent results are now presented.

Spectrum of antiviral activity

BVDU inhibits the replication of herpes simplex virus type 1 (HSV-1) and varicella zoster virus (VZV) with similar efficiency [MIC (minimal inhibitory concentration) for both viruses in human diploid fibroblasts $\simeq$ 0.01 μg/ml]. BVDU is less inhibitory for herpes simplex virus type 2 (HSV-2) (MIC $\simeq$ 1 μg/ml) and vaccinia virus (MIC $\simeq$ 1-10 μg/ml). Preliminary findings (H. Schellekens) indicate that it is not active against cytomegalovirus.

Mechanism of action

The selectivity of BVDU as an antiherpes agent is based upon a specific inhibition of viral DNA synthesis: for example, in primary rabbit kidney (PRK) cells infected with HSV-1, BVDU completely shut off DNA synthesis at a concentration of 0.1 µg/ml, while DNA synthesis in uninfected PRK cells was not affected unless the drug concentration was raised to 100 µg/ml. At least two factors appear to contribute to the selectivity of the drug as an anti-herpes agent:

(1) The human cytosol thymidine kinase (TK) has a negligible affinity for BVDU whereas the latter has a high affinity for the HSV-1 and VZV-induced TKs which thus restricts the phosphorylation of BVDU to the virus-infected cell $[K_I$ (µM) for human cytosol thymidine kinase for BVDU,> 400; for HSV-1, 0.15; for VZV, 0.06; Y.-C. Cheng, personal communication].

(2) The 5'-triphosphate of BVDU has been synthesized chemically and its effects on the herpes-induced and cellular DNA polymerases tested. Under optimum assay conditions for each enzyme, the triphosphate at a concentration of 1 µM inhibited HSV-1 DNA polymerase by 60% while inhibiting the cellular DNA polymerases $\underline{\alpha}$ and $\underline{\beta}$ by only 9% and 3% respectively. The inhibition was shown to be competitive with the natural substrate dTTP. The K_m for dTTP and the K_I for BVDU triphosphate for the HSV-1 induced DNA polymerase were 0.66 µM and 0.25 µM respectively. The compound was shown to be inhibitory even after initiation of the enzyme reaction and it is most likely that BVDU would be incorporated into the viral DNA.

Thus BVDU exerts its selective inhibition of the viral DNA replication in two ways: firstly it is phosphorylated only in virus-infected cells by the virus-induced thymidine kinase and secondly the 5'-triphosphate is a preferential inhibitor of the virus-induced DNA polymerase.

Animal model infections

In athymic nude mice, BVDU has proved to be efficacious in suppressing the development of HSV-1 skin lesions, and mortality associated therewith, whether the drug was administered topically (as a 1% ointment) or systemically (at 60 mg/kg). In rabbits, BVDU proved superior to IDU in promoting the healing of superficial herpetic keratitis, when applied as eye drops (or ointment) at either 0.1% or 0.5%, and recent findings indicate that BVDU, when administered as 0.1 or 0.5% eye drops, is also highly effective in suppressing the development of deep stromal herpetic keratitis in rabbits.

Pharmacokinetics

BVDU is readily absorbed when given orally to either mice or rabbits: peak serum drug levels are attained within 30 min (mice) or 90 min (rabbits) and amount to approximately 40 μg/ml (mice) or 10 μg/ml (rabbits) after oral administration of 100 - 150 mg/kg. Active blood drug levels are sustained for several hours : for example, a blood drug level of 0.2 - 0.3 μg/ml was detected 7 hours after oral administration of BVDU at 135 mg/kg to rabbits. Drug levels attained in the bile and urine (of rabbits) were about ten times higher than those achieved in the blood stream, suggesting that the drug is actively excreted by the liver and kidney.

Toxicity

No untoward effects have been noted in young NMRI mice which were treated intraperitoneally with BVDU at 250 - 500 mg/kg daily for four consecutive weeks (5 times a week) : these mice developed normally, gained as much weight as control mice and did not reveal pathological changes in any of the organs (brain, heart, lung, liver, kidney, spleen, thymus, lymph nodes, gut and gonads) that were examined histologically. Neither were there any significant haematological disturbances. For those mice that received BVDU at 500 - 1000 mg/kg/day in their drinking-water during 20 consecutive days, there was a slight delay in growth, which could at least partially be explained by a reduced water intake. Histological examination at the end of the treatment period revealed no pathological alterations, except for the liver parenchym which showed a diffuse fatty degeneration and for the testis which showed a block at the maturation of spermatocytes to spermatids. The liver alterations were more pronounced in female than in male mice. However, they were not accompanied by an increase in the blood transaminase levels. Both the liver and spermiogenesis disturbances regressed after termination of BVDU treatment.

Clinical observations

Several clinical trials have recently been initiated, i.e. with 0.1 % BVDU eye drops in the treatment of superficial and stromal herpetic keratitis, with a 0.1 % BVDU ointment in the treatment of recurrent herpes labialis, with a 1 % BVDU ointment in the treatment of herpetic skin lesions, and with a 1 % BVDU solution (at pH 9.5), applied through iontophoresis in the treatment of localized herpes zoster. BVDU will also be administered orally to cancer patients with systemic herpes simplex or herpes zoster infections.

Some of these trials (i.e. those with herpes labialis) are carried out on a placebo-controlled double-blind basis and the results cannot be disclosed yet. However, for treatment of patients with herpetic keratitis we have so far only performed open trials. More than twenty patients with either superficial or stromal keratitis, that had become resistant to IDU or araA (vidarabine, adenine arabinoside) therapy, have now been treated with BVDU (0.1% eye drops) and they all responded favourably : within 24 hours of BVDU treatment they felt a marked relief of discomfort, their cornea ulcers healed briskly and even the stromal lesions resolved under BVDU therapy, so that some patients with deep stromal keratitis could be taken off corticosteroids.

ACKNOWLEDGEMENTS

The work described here has taken place over a period of many years in several laboratories. Most of those scientists involved have been acknowledged in the text or in the references and we would like to express our appreciation for all the interest and dedication they have shown.

REFERENCES

1. Evans, C.H., Jones, A.S. and Walker, R.T. (1973) Tetrahedron 29, 1611.
2. Chelton, E.T.J., Evans, C.H., Jones, A.S. and Walker, R.T. (1973) Biochim. Biophys. Acta 312, 38.
3. Jones, A.S., Stephenson, G.P. and Walker, R.T. (1974) Nucleic Acids Res. 1, 105.
4. Bleackley, R.C., Jones, A.S. and Walker, R.T. (1975) Nucleic Acids Res. 2, 683.
5. Jones, A.S. and Walker, R.T. (1975) Nucleic Acids Res. Sp. Publ. No. 1, s1.
6. Bleackley, R.C., Jones, A.S. and Walker, R.T. (1976) Tetrahedron 32, 2795.
7. Barr, P.J., Jones, A.S. and Walker, R.T. (1976) Nucleic Acids Res. 3, 2845.
8. Jones, A.S., Serafinowski, P. and Walker, R.T. (1977) Tetrahedron Letters 2459.
9. Barr, P.J., Jones, A.S., Serafinowski, P. and Walker, R.T. (1978) J. Chem. Soc. Perkin Trans. 1 1263.
10. Bleackley, R.C., Jones, A.S. and Walker, R.T. (1978) Improved and New Synthetic Procedures, Methods and Techniques, Part 2, L.B. Townsend and R.S. Tipson eds., John Wiley & Sons Inc. N.Y. pp 927.
11. Jones, A.S., Stephenson, G.P. and Walker, R.T. (1979) Tetrahedron 35, 1125.
12. Jones, A.S. Verhelst, G. and Walker, R.T. (1979) Tetrahedron Letters 4415.
13. Barr, P.J., Bohacek, L., Jones, A.S. and Walker, R.T. (1979) J. Labelled Cmpds. and Radiopharmaceuticals 16, 909.
14. Chelton, E.T.J., Jones, A.S. and Walker, R.T. (1979) Biochem. J. 181, 783.
15. Chelton, E.T.J., Duggan, M.J., Hunston, R.N., Jones, A.S., O'Leary, M.K., Overton, D.J. and Walker, R.T. (1980) Biochem. J. 187, 257.
16. Biała, E., Jones, A.S. and Walker, R.T. (1980) Tetrahedron 36, 155.
17. Hamor, T.A., O'Leary, M.K. and Walker, R.T. (1977) Acta Cryst. B33, 1218.
18. Hamor, T.A., O'Leary, M.K. and Walker, R.T. (1978) Acta Cryst. B34, 1627.
19. Barr, P.J., Hamor, T.A. and Walker, R.T. (1978) Acta Cryst. B34, 2799.
20. Walker, R.T., Barr, P.J., De Clercq, E., Descamps, J., Jones, A.S. and Serafinowski, P. (1978) Nucleic Acids Res. Sp. Publ. No. 4, s103.
21. De Clercq, E., Descamps, J., Barr, P.J., Jones, A.S., Serafinowski, P., Walker, R.T., Huang, G.F., Torrence, P.F., Schmidt, C.L., Mertes, M.P.,

Kulikowski, T. and Shugar, D. (1979) Antimetabolites in Biochemistry, Biology and Medicine, J. Skoda and P. Langen eds., Pergamon, Oxford pp 275.

22. De Clercq, E., Descamps, P., De Somer, P., Barr, P.J., Jones, A.S. and Walker, R.T. (1979) Proc. Natl. Acad. Sci. USA 76, 2947.

23. De Clercq, E., Descamps, P., De Somer, P., Barr, P.J., Jones, A.S. and Walker, R.T. (1979) Antimicrobial Ag. Chemother. 16, 234.

24. Descamps, J., De Clercq, E., Barr, P.J., Jones, A.S., Walker, R.T., Torrence, P.F., and Shugar, D. (1979) Antimicrobial Ag. Chemother. 16, 680.

25. Maudgal, P.C., De Clercq, E., Descamps, J., Missotten, L., De Somer, P., Busson, R., Vanderhaeghe, H., Verhelst, G., Walker, R.T. and Jones, A.S. (1980) Antimicrobial Ag. Chemother. 17, 8.

26. De Clercq, E., Descamps, J., Verhelst, G., Walker, R.T., Jones, A.S. Torrence, P.F. and Shugar, D. (1980) J. Infect. Diseases In the press.

27. De Clercq, E., Descamps, J., Maudgal, P.C., Missotten, L., Leyten, R., Verhelst, G., Jones, A.S., Walker, R.T., Busson, R., Vanderhaeghe, H. and De Somer, P. (1980) Developments in Antiviral Chemotherapy L.H. Collier and J. Oxford eds., Academic Press, London, In the press.

28. De Clercq, E., Balzarini, J., Torrence, P.F., Mertes, M.P., Schmidt, C.L., Shugar, D., Barr, P.J., Jones, A.S., Verhelst, G. and Walker, R.T. Cancer Res. Submitted.

29. Fissekis, J.D. and Sweet, F. (1973) J. Org. Chem. 38, 264.

30. Fissekis, J.D. and Sweet, F. (1973) J. Org. Chem. 38, 1963.

31. Sharma, R.A. and Bobek, M. (1975) J. Org. Chem. 40, 2377.

32. Bärwolff, D. and Langen, P. (1975) Nucleic Acids Res. Sp. Publ. No. 1, s29.

33. Perman, J., Sharma, R.A. and Bobek, M. (1976) Tetrahedron Letters 2427.

34. Matthes, E., Bärwolff, D., Preussel, B. and Langen, P. (1978) Antimetabolites in Biochemistry, Biology and Medicine, J. Skoda and P. Langen eds., Pergamon, Oxford pp 115.

35. Langen, P. and Bärwolff, D. (1975) Biochem. Pharm. 24, 1907.

36. Cheng, Y.-C., Domin, B.A., Sharma, R.A. and Bobek, M. (1976) Antimicrobial Ag. Chemother. 10, 119.

37. Perman, J., Sharma, R.A. and Bobek, M. (1977) Chemistry and Biology of Nucleosides and Nucleotides, R.E. Harmon, R.K. Robins and L.B. Townsend eds., Academic Press, New York.

38. Bergstrom, D.E. and Ruth, J.L. (1976) J. Amer. Chem. Soc. 98, 1587.

39. Bergstrom, D.E. and Ruth, J.L. (1977) J. Carbohydrates, Nucleosides, Nucleotides, 4, 257.

40. Bergstrom, D.E. and Ogawa, M.K. (1978) J. Amer. Chem. Soc. 100, 8106.

41. Elion, G.B., Furman, P.A., Fyfe, J.A., De Miranda, P., Beauchamp, L. and Schaeffer, H.J. (1977) Proc. Natl. Acad. Sci. USA 74, 5716.

42. Watanabe, K.A., Reichman, U., Hirota, K., Lopez, C. and Fox, J.J. (1979) J. Med. Chem. 22, 21.

Nucleic Acids Research

DNA damage induced with near-ultraviolet light irradiation in the presence of quinoxaline-1,4-dioxide

Kazuo Negishi, Yasuko Arao, Naomi Oka and Hikoya Hayatsu

Faculty of Pharmaceutical Sciences, Okayama University, Tsushima, Okayama 700, Japan

ABSTRACT

When Bacillus subtilis transforming DNA was irradiated with near-ultra-violet light in the presence of quinoxaline-1,4-dioxide, the activity of DNA decreased rapidly. This loss of activity was ascribed to damages on DNA that lead to chain cleavages of the molecule. A feature of this phototoxic action of the reagent is that it takes place in nitrogen atmosphere and is inhibited by oxygen.

It is well known that many dyes, e.g., methylene blue, sensitize nucleic acids to visible and near-ultraviolet light. Their sensitizing action, i.e. the photodynamic action, requires oxygen during irradiation[1]. Photosensitizing action that does not require oxygen is also known: compounds such as psoralen are covalently attached to nucleic acids under irradiation with near-ultraviolet light[2]. Here we wish to report a new type of photosensitizing action caused by quinoxaline-1,4-dioxide (Ia) and its derivative Carbadox (2-formylquinoxaline-1,4-dioxide carbomethoxyhydrazone)(Ib). Quinoxaline-1,4-dioxide and Carbadox are bactericidal agents and the latter is currently being used as a feed additive for swine to promote growth. We have recently shown that these two drugs are mutagenic to Salmonella typhimurium[3,4].

Ia R= -H

Ib R= -CH=NNHCOOCH3

Experiments were performed using transforming DNA extracted from met⁺ Bacillus subtilis. The DNA was irradiated with Black Light (>300 nm) in the presence of quinoxaline-1,4-dioxide or Carbadox under nitrogen atmosphere.

Transforming activity of the DNA was assayed on met⁻ bacteria. The activity
was shown to be rapidly lost as a function of the irradiation time.
Surprisingly, this phototoxic action of reagents was not observable when the
reactions were carried out in the air or in an oxygen atmosphere.

For the elucidation of the inactivation mechanism, DNA treated with
Carbadox plus light in the nitrogen atmosphere was analyzed with alkaline
sucrose density gradient sedimentation. The sedimentation rate of the
treated DNA was significantly smaller than that of the untreated DNA. The
drug alone or the light alone had little or no effect on the rate. These
results showed that Carbadox plus light caused strand-breaks and/or alkali-
labile bonds on the DNA. This reaction was also inhibited by air. This
lesion on the DNA was therefore likely to be the cause of the inactivation.

REFERENCES

1 Simon, M.I. and Vunakis, H.V. (1964) Arch. Biochem. Biophys. 105, 197-206.
2 Cole, R.S. (1971) Biochim. Biophys. Acta 254, 30-39.
3 Hashimoto, T., Negishi, T., Namba, T., Hayakawa, S. and Hayatsu, H. (1979) Chem. Pharm. Bull. (Tokyo) 27, 1954-1956.
4 Negishi, T., Tanaka, K. and Hayatsu, H. (1980) Chem. Pharm. Bull. (Tokyo) 28, 1347-1349.

Reactions of potent mutagens, 3-amino-1-methyl-5H-pyrido[4,3-b]indole (Trp-P-2) and 2-amino-6-methyl-dipyrido[1,2-a:3',2'-d]imidazole (Glu-P-1) with nucleic acid

Yuichi Hashimoto, Koichi Shudo, Masazumi Imamura and Toshihiko Okamoto

Faculty of Pharmaceutical Sciences, University of Tokyo, Hongo, Bunkyo-ku, Tokyo, Japan

ABSTRACT
    Two potent mutagens, 3-amino-1-methyl-5H-pyrido[4,3-b]in-
dole (Trp-P-2), isolated from a tryptophan pyrolysate, and 2-
amino-6-methyldipyrido[1,2-a:3',2'-d]imidazole (Glu-P-1), isolated from a glutamic acid pyrolysate, modified calf thymus DNA in
the presence of rat liver microsomes.   The major base modified
by Trp-P-2 was identified with 3-(8-guanyl)amino-1-methyl-5H-py-
rido[4,3-b]indole.   The major base modified by Glu-P-1 was i-
dentified with 2-(8-guanyl)amino-6-methyldipyrido[1,2-a:3',2'-d]
imidazole.   N-acetoxy-Glu-P-1 efficiently modified DNA without
microsomes.

INTRODUCTION
    The induction of mutagenesis or carcinogenesis is believed
to be related to the binding of the activated mutagens or carci-
nogens with DNA.   Elucidation of modified DNA structure is essential in order to understand a molecular basis for alteration
of gene expression in mutagenesis or carcinogenesis.   This
paper describes modification of DNA and structure elucidation of
modified bases by very potent mutagens, 3-amino-1-methyl-5H-pyri-
do[4,3-b]indole (Trp-P-2) and 2-amino-6-methyldipyrido[1,2-a:3',
2'-d]imidazole (Glu-P-1) isolated from pyrolysates of tryptophan
and glutamic acid, respectively.

Trp-P-2   Glu-P-1

RAT LIVER MEDIATED BINDING OF TRP-P-2 WITH DNA [1]

Binding of the potent mutagen Trp-P-2 to DNA was confirmed by an experiment using tritiated Trp-P-2. The radioactivity of Trp-P-2 was found in the DNA treated with Trp-P-2 in the presence of rat liver microsomes. The binding was very tight and was not affected by reprecipitation, dialysis, or gel filtration. Since no binding was observed in control experiments without microsomes or with heated enzyme, the binding of Trp-P-2 requires an activation enzyme system. From the radioactivity, the amount of Trp-P-2 bound to DNA was calculated to be about 60 µM/Mol P, and the binding increased to 230 µM/Mol P on three successive incubations of DNA with microsomes and Trp-P-2. No radioactivity was found in the polyribonucleotides, poly A, poly C and poly U on incubation with or without microsomes. Trp-P-2 bound significantly to poly G, but a partial tight physical binding to a self coagulated poly G could not be ruled out.

STRUCTURE OF A MODIFIED BASE OF TRP-P-2-BOUND DNA. [2]

The treatment of calf thymus DNA as above with Trp-P-2 in the presence of rat liver microsomes gave a modified DNA . The DNA was hydrolysed by DNase I from beef pancreas at 37° for 6 hr and after changing the pH of the solution to 9.0, phosphodiesterase from Crotalus adamanteus venom, Type II, was added and incubated at 37° for 6 hr. To the digested solution was added alkaline phosphatase from calf intestinal mucosa, Type I, and the mixture was incubated at 37° for 48 hr. The deoxyribonucleosides thus obtained were subjected to Sephadex LH 20 column chromatography, eluted with water-methanol. Fluorescent fractions were collected and lyophilized. Trp-P-2-bound bases were obtained by acid hydrolysis of the fluorescent fractions (0.1 N HCl). The mixture was analyzed by liquid chromatography. Three peaks were observed.

The major peak was identified with 3-(8-guanyl)amino-1-methyl-5H-pyrido[4,3-b]indole, which was prepared by the nucleophilic substitution by Trp-P-2 at the 8 position of 3-acetoxyguanine in DMSO. The identification was performed by four different LC systems, and fluorescence and excitation spectra at different acidities, and comparison of chemical reactivity. The structure of the synthetic product was proved by high resolution mass spectroscopy, carbon and proton nmr, and chemical degradation to Trp-P-2 and uric acid. The position of the binding nitrogen was confirmed by the isolation of 1,2,5-trimethyl-3-oxo-3H-pyrido[4,3-b]indole as the alkaline hydrolysis product of the permethylated compound.

STRUCTURE OF A MODIFIED BASE OF GLU-P-1-BOUND DNA [3]

Glu-P-1-bound DNA was obtained by three repeated incubations of calf thymus DNA with Glu-P-1 in the presence of rat liver microsomes with NADPH generating system. The modified DNA was hydrolyzed by DNase I, phosphodiesterase, and alkaline phosphatase, successively, as described in the above case. Sephadex LH 20 column chromatography gave fluorescent nucleoside fractions accompanying fluorescent base fractions, the last being obtained by acid hydrolysis of the nucleoside fractions.

The major modified base was identified with 2-(8-guanyl)-amino-6-methyldipyrido[1,2-a:3',2'-d]imidazole, which was prepared from Glu-P-1 and 3-acetoxyguanine. Chromatographic and spectral identifications were sufficient. The same compound could be prepared from 2,4,5-triamino-6-hydroxypyrimidine and 2-carboethoxyamino-6-methyldipyrido[1,2-a:3',2'-d]imidazole, which proved the structure unambiguously.

In summary, both mutagens Trp-P-2 and Glu-P-1 modified DNA in a similar fashion, that is, by the covalent bond formation between the amino nitrogens of mutagens and 8 position of guanine base.

MODIFICATION OF DNA BY N-ACETOXY GLU-P-1 [4]

The establishment of the modified base structures strongly suggested that the activated forms of Trp-P-2 and Glu-P-1 by microsomes were hydroxylamines metabolically formed by oxidation.

Analyses of metabolic products of Trp-P-2 and Glu-P-1 showed the major metabolites from these mutagens were N-OH-Trp-P-2 and N-OH-Glu-P-1, respectively.

N-hydroxy-Glu-P-1, however, reacted with DNA only slightly. N-Acetoxy-Glu-P-1 readily and efficiently bound with DNA and a complementary dinucleotide, guanyl-cytidine, but not with guanosine.

REFERENCES

1. Hashimoto,Y., Takeda,K., Shudo,K., Okamoto,T.,Sugimura,T., Kosuge,T. (1978) Chem.Biol.Interact.,23 137-140.
2. Hashimoto, Y., Shudo,K., Okamoto,T. (1979) Chem.Pharm. Bull. 27 1058-1060.
3. Idem, (1979) ibid, 27 2532-2534.
4. Idem, (1980) Biochem. Biophys.Res. Comm. 92 971-976.

Characterization of nuclear 5.7S RNAs of mouse cells

Nobuyuki Kato and Fumio Harada

Virology Division, National Cancer Center Research Institute, Tsukiji 5-1-1, Chuo-ku, Tokyo, Japan

The nuclei of eukaryotic cells contain some unique species of small molecular weight RNAs (snRNAs) with sedimentation coefficients of 4 to 8S (1,2). The nucleotide sequences of some of them were determined (3-6), but little is known on their function.

Recently Lerner and Steitz reported that the serum of the patients with systemic lupus erythematosus reacts with nuclear ribonucleoproteins which contain six different snRNAs (7). Since one of the snRNAs (U1a) has a sequence complementary to the terminal sequences of the intervening regions of mRNA precursors, they proposed that these snRNAs may be involved in the splicing mechanisms (8).

We have recently isolated a series of 4.5S RNAs from murine retroviruses, virus infected mouse cells and uninfected rodent cells (9,10). These RNAs are specifically associated with viral and cellular poly(A)-containing RNAs. These RNAs also contain the sequence which is complementary to the splice junctions of mRNA presursors (11).

To clarify whether other snRNAs have similar sequences complementary to the splice junctions, we purified and characterized 5.7S RNAs of mouse cells.

We purified nuclear RNA from ^{32}P-labeled mouse lymphoma cells L1210 and separated it by two dimensional polyacrylamide gel electrophoresis. 17 distinct snRNAs were obtained by this method. Each snRNA was analyzed by RNase T1 fingerprinting and compared with published fingerprints. Thus, 5.7S RNA was assigned as U4 RNA of Lerner and Steitz (7).

5.7S RNA was further separated to 5.7S RNAs a and b by the

electrophoresis in 16% polyacrylamide gel containing 7M urea. Both molecules gave very similar but not identical fingerprints. In preliminary experiments, we found that each 5.7S RNA consists of about 145 nucleotide residues with one mole each of $m_3^{2,2,7}G$, Am, Cm and unidentified nucleoside Nm and 3 moles of Ψ as modified nucleosides. The 5'-terminus is $m_3^{2,2,7}GpppNmpCp$ and the 3'-terminus is A-C-U-G$_{OH}$.

REFERENCES

1. Ro-Choi, T. S. and Busch, H. (1974) in the Cell Nucleus, Busch, H. ed., Vol. III, pp. 151-208, Academic Press, New York
2. Zieve, G. and Penman, S. (1976) Cell 8, 19-31
3. Ro-Choi, T. S., Reddy, R., Henning, D., Takano, T., Taylor, C. W. and Busch, H. (1972) J. Biol. Chem. 247, 3205-3222
4. Reddy, R., Ro-Choi, T. S., Henning, D. and Busch, H. (1974) J. Biol. Chem. 249, 6486-6494
5. Shibata, H., Ro-Choi, T. S., Reddy, R., Choi, Y. C., Henning, D. and Busch, H. (1975) J. Biol. Chem. 250, 3909-3920
6. Reddy, R., Henning, D. and Busch, H. (1979) J. Biol. Chem. 254, 11097-11105
7. Lerner, M. R. and Steitz, J. A. (1979) Proc. Natl. Acad. Sci. USA 76, 5495-5499
8. Lerner, M. R., Boyle, J. A., Mount, S. M., Wolin, S. L. and Steitz, J. A. (1980) Nature 283, 220-224
9. Harada, F. and Ikawa, Y. (1979) Nucleic Acids Res. 7, 895-908
10. Harada, F., Kato, N. and Hoshino, H. (1979) Nucleic Acids Res. 7, 909-917
11. Harada, F. and Kato, N. (1980) Nucleic Acids Res. 8, 1273-1285

Nucleotide sequences and evolutional aspect of 5S ribosomal RNAs from Lingula and silkworm

Hiroyuki Komiya, Makoto Kawakami, Nobuyoshi Shimizu and Shosuke Takemura

Institute of Molecular Biology, School of Science, Nagoya University, Nagoya 464, Japan

ABSTRACT

Ribosomal 5S RNAs were highly purified from the total tissues of Lingula anatina and the posterior silk glands of Bombyx mori. The nucleotide sequences of the RNAs were determined by a chemical method for rapidly sequencing on gels of 3' end-labeled RNA, with the aid of conventional sequence analysis of the complete RNase digests of the unlabeled RNAs. By comparing the sequences with those of several animal and Chlorella 5S rRNAs, a phylogenic tree of these 5S rRNAs was constructed.

INTRODUCTION

Ribosomal 5S RNA is useful for investigating an early stage of evolution, since all organisms have this RNA usually in one molecular species, sequence analysis of this RNA has become very easier than ever by a post-labeling and a rapid sequencing-on-gel methods, and also the rate of the base substitution is reasonably slow. While the nucleotide sequences of about 70 5S rRNA species from many prokaryotes, yeasts, plants, and vertebrates are now known, Drosophila melanogaster is the only invertebrate whose 5S rRNA has so far been sequenced[1]. We have determined the sequences of 5S rRNAs of Lingula anatina and Bombyx mori to investigate the molecular evolution of invertebrate 5S rRNAs.

MATERIALS AND METHODS

The total tissues of Lingula (400 g) were crushed, homogenized in 1.2 l of 0.02 M Tris-HCl (pH 7.5), 0.1 M NaCl, 0.005 M MgCl$_2$ and 0.1 % bentonite, and treated with 1.5 l of water-saturated phenol. After the aqueous layer was further treated with phenol twice, 5S rRNA was purified by the same method as described previously[2]. A low molecular weight RNA fraction was obtained from the posterior

silk glands of the 5th instar of <u>Bombyx</u> <u>mori</u> as described before[3].
Silkworm 5S rRNA was purified from this fraction by gel filtration
on a column of Sephadex G100 and electrophoresis on a discontinuous
polyacrylamide slab gel[4].

The 3' end of the RNAs were labeled with $[^{32}P]$pCp and T_4-RNA
ligase. The nucleotide sequences were analyzed by the chemical
sequencing method of Peattie[5]. Sequences of a few regions still
remained ambiguously. To solve these, oligonucleotides in the
complete digests of the unlabeled RNAs with RNases T_1 and A were
also sequenced by conventional column chromatography[2].

RESULTS AND DISCUSSION

Figure 1 shows the autoradiographs of 3' end-labeled silkworm
5S rRNA sequenced chemically. It was possible to read-out the
sequence from the labeled 3' end to somewhere about position 4.

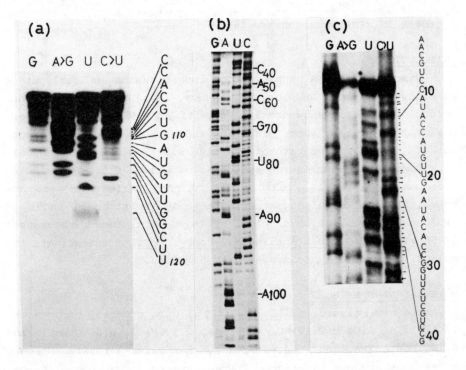

Fig. 1. Autoradiographs of 3' end-labeled silkworm 5S rRNA
sequenced chemically and run on a thin polyacrylamide gels.
a, b, and c; The 3' end region (25 % gel), the internal region
(12 % gel), and the 5' end region (12 % gel), respectively.

The complete RNase T_1 digest of the unlabeled RNA contained pGp and C-C-A-A-C-Gp. The latter overlaps with positions 4 to 7 sequenced chemically. Thus the sequence of the 5' end region was established to be pG-C-C-A-A-C-G-. Figure 1b can be read as if the sequence at positions 85 to 90 were -U-G-G-U-G-A-. However the result of analysis of the RNase A digest suggested to be -U-G-G-G-U-G-A- for this region. Peattie also observed that the labeled fragment corresponding to cleavage at G89 in Saccharomyces 5S rRNA was very faint[5]. The results of sequence analyses of other oligonucleotides from the RNase T_1 and A digests were compatible with the chemical analysis. The total sequence was then established as shown in Fig. 2. Lingula 5S rRNA was also sequenced similarly (Fig. 2).

Table I shows the numbers of different nucleotides between the corresponding positions in the 5S rRNAs of several animals and Chlorella. Since the numbers represent the mutation distances between the RNAs, it is possible to construct a phylogenic tree of these RNAs by the method of Fitch and Margoliash[6] as shown in Fig. 3. The branching pattern agrees with the morphological classification; Lingula and insects belong to Postostomia and the vertebrates to Deuterostomia. The tree shows that, after the divergence of the two groups, the insects and Lingula 5S rRNAs branched. Although Lingula has been morphologically highly conserved ever since the Cambrian period, the 5S rRNA has accepted mutation at about the same rate as vertebrate 5S rRNAs. On the other hand, the insect 5S rRNAs have mutated at a considerably faster rate than other animal 5S rRNAs. This might be partly due to shorter generation times of insects than those of other animals.

```
                  10        20        30        40        50
Silkworm 5S rRNA  pGCCAACGUCCAUACCAUGUUGAAUACACCGGUUCUCGUCCGAUCACCGAA
Lingula  5S rRNA  GUCUACGACCAUACCACGUUGAAAGCACCGGUUCUCGUCCGAUCACCGAA

     60        70        80        90       100       110       120
GUCAAGCAACAUCGGGCGUGGUCAGUACUUGGAUGGGUGACCGCCUGGGAACACCACGUGAUGUUGGCUU
GUUAAGCAACGUCGGGCCAGGUUAGUACUUGGAUGGGUGACCGCCUGGGAAUACCUGGUGCCGUAGACA
```

Fig. 2. Nucleotide sequences of silkworm and Lingula 5S rRNAs.

Table I. The numbers of nucleotide substitutions between 5S rRNAs from several animals and <u>Chlorella</u>.

	Human[7]	Rainbow trout	<u>Drosophila</u>	Silkworm	<u>Lingula</u>
Rainbow trout[2]	8				
<u>Drosophila</u>[1]	26	26			
Silkworm	27	25	16		
<u>Lingula</u>	20	24	22	20	
Chlorella[8]	45	49	54	53	47

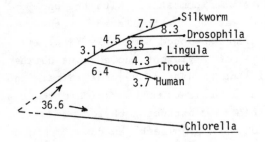

Fig. 3. A phylogenic tree of 5S rRNAs constructed from Table I by the method of Fitch and Margoliash[6]. The numbers represent the mutation distances.

REFERENCES

1. Benhamou, J. and Jordan, B.R. (1976) FEBS Lett. 62, 146-149
2. Komiya, H. and Takemura, S. (1979) J. Biochem. 86, 1067-1080
3. Kawakami, M. and Shimura, K. (1973) J. Biochem. 74, 33-40
4. Philippsen, P. and Zachau, H.G. (1972) Biochim. Biophys. Acta 277, 523-538
5. Peattie, D.A. (1979) Proc. Natl. Acad. Sci. U.S.A. 76, 1760-1764
6. Fitch, W.M. and Margoliash, E. (1969) Science 155, 279-284
7. Forget, B.G. and Weissman, S.M. (1969) J. Biol. Chem. 244, 3148-3165
8. Jordan, B.R., Galling, G. and Jourdan, R. (1974) J. Mol. Biol. 87, 205-225

Magnetic circular dichroism and circular dichroism of some nucleosides

Masahiro Hatano, Akira Kaito, Akio Tajiri, Toru Ueda* and Susumu Shibuya*

Chemical Research Institute of Non-aqueous Solutions, Tohoku University, Sendai 980, and
*Faculty of Pharmaceutical Science, Hokkaido University, Sapporo 060, Japan

ABSTRACT

The magnetic circular dichroism and circular dichroism
spectra of cytidine, isocytidine, 2,5'-O-cyclo-2',3'-O-isopro-
pylidine uridine, and 2,2'-O-cylcouridine were measured in the
wavenumber region of 30000 -50000 cm^{-1}.   On the basis of the
experimental results, the tautomerism of cytidine and isocytidine was discussed.   The transition energies, the oscillator
strengths, and the Faraday parameters were calculated within
the framework of the INDO approximation.   The calculated
results are in good agreement with the experimental results.
And then the spectral assignment of the pyrimidine nucleosides,
together with those of cytosine and isocytosine, were discussed
on the basis of the experimental and theoretical results.

INTRODUCTION

Magnetic circular dichroism(MCD) spectra of purine and
pyrimidine derivatives, which are the consistuents of nucleic
acids, have been extensively studied by many investigators[1-4].
Some overlapping absorption bands have been resolved in the
MCD spectra and the valuable information on the electronic
structure of these compounds has been obtained.   Recently,
the quantum mechanical calculations on the MCD of some purine
derivatives[4,5] and pyrimidine derivatives[6] have been reported.
On the other hand, the study of the circular dichroism(CD) of
nucleoside derivatives has been a subject of considerable
interest, because CD is a helpful tool for spectral and conformational analysis of nucleoside derivatives.   Miles et al[7]
have identified the four electronic transitions in the CD spectra
of uracil and cytosine nucleoside derivatives and related them
to the $^1B_{2u}$, $^1B_{1u}$, and $^1E_{1u}$ bands of benzene.   They have also
proposed an empirical diagram of the molecular ellipticity of
the lowest $\pi^*\leftarrow\pi$ transition as a function of the sugar-base
torsion angle, ϕ_{CN}.   They have also calculated the rotational
strengths of some pyrimidine nucleosides on the basis of the
bond-bond coupled oscillatory theory[8,9].   It has been shown
that the rotational strengths of the lowest $\pi^*\leftarrow\pi$ transitions of
pyrimidine nucleosides are sensitive to the torsional angle;
positive for anti-conformation and negative for syn-conformation.

From the proton and fluorine magnetic resonance spectra of pyrimidine nucleoside derivatives, it has been suggested that pyrimidine nucleosides take C_3, endo-sugar and anti-sugar-base conformation[10]. The CD spectra of pyrimidine cyclonucleosides with fixed structure have been studied by several investigators[7] Miles et al.[7] have assigned the small lowest CD band of cyclo-uridine at about 37000 cm^{-1} to the $^1B_{2u}$ band. They have also reported that the CD of the cyclouridine analogues is in contra-diction with thier diagrams in which the molecular ellipticity of the $^1B_{2u}$ band is drawn as a fuction of ϕ_{CN}. On the other hand, Ulbricht and his coworkers[11] have shown from the solvent shift of the CD band that the small lowest CD band of pyrimidine cyclonucleosides is originated from a $\pi^* \leftarrow \pi$ transition. Thus, the interpretation of the CD spectra of pyrimidine cyclonucleo-sides are not clarified.

In the present paper we measured the CD and MCD spectra of cytidine, isocytidine, 2,5'-O-cyclo-2',3'-O-isopropylidene uri-dine, and 2,2'-O-cyclouridine together with cytosine and iso-cytosine, in the ultraviolet region. We also calculated the rotational strengths and the Faraday B terms of these pyrimidine nucleosides using the wavefunctions obtained by the intermediate neglect of the differential overlap(INDO) approximation[12-16]. And the spectral assignments of these CD and MCD bands were discussed.

THEORETICAL

In order to find out the preferred conformation of cytidine and isocytidine, the potential energies were calculated as a fuction of the torsional angle, ϕ_{CN}, around the glycoside bond. In this work, the potential energy was assumed to be the sum of the nonbonded van der Waals interactions and the electrostatic interactions. The nonbonded interactions were evaluated by using the Lennard-Jones 6 -12 potential functions. The electrostatic interactions were calculated by the Coulomb's laws. The atomic charges were calculated by the INDO/S procedures and the effective dielectric constant was assumed to be 4.0.

Conformation of the sugar of the derivatives was assumed to be C_2' endo and C_3' endo. Atomic coordinates of the conform-ers were taken from X-ray crystallographical data of cytidine[17] and formycin[18], respectively. Two conformations around glycosidic bond were considered for 2,5'-O-cyclo-2',3'-O-iso-propylidene uridine. One is endo-form in which O(2) oxygen is positioned almost over the center of the furanose ring. Another is exo-form whose O(2) oxygen is placed above O(1') oxygen atom of the furanose ring. In the crystalline state only endo-form has been shown to be present[19]. The bond lengths and bond angles of 2,5'-O-cyclo-2',3'-O-isopropylidene uridine were taken from the data of the X-ray analysis[19]. The dihedral angles, C(6)-N(1)-C(1')-O(1'), of endo- and exo-forms are 113.8° and 162.8°, respectively.

The oscillator strengths and the Faraday B terms were calculated within the framework of the INDO/S procedure[15,16]. The parameters of the calculation were shown in the previous papers[15,16]. Configuration interaction among singly excited

configurations below 9 eV was taken into account.   The
Faraday B terms were calculated by the dipole length method,
as shown in the previous papers[12-16].   On the other hand,
the dipole velocity method was used for the calculation of the
rotational strengths in order to avoid the origin dependence
of the calculated rotational strengths[12].   The LCAO-MO coefficients regarding the orthogonalized INDO atomic orbital
basis were deorthogonalized by the inverse Löwdin transformation
and atomic integrals were calculated using Slater atomic
orbitals[12-16].   However, the calculated oscillator strengths
of the $\pi^*\leftarrow n$ transitions of the azines are very sensitive to the
one center integral, $<2s|\nabla_x|2p_x>$, in the diople velocity method.
Therefore, the value of the one center integral was scaled
down by the adjustable parameter, k.   In this work k was
chosen to be 0.555, so as to reproduce the oscillator strengths
of the azines.

RESULTS AND DISCUSSION

     The conformational energy curves of cytidine and isocytidine
were obtained as functions of the sugar-base torsion angle, ϕ_{CN}.
We used the usual convention for ϕ_{CN}, that is, if C(6) atom
eclipses O(1') atom, $\phi_{CN}=0°$.   If the base plane is rotated
counterclockwise against C(1')-O(1') bond, when viewed from C(1')
atom toward N(1) atom, the rotation is in the positive direction.
The anti-conformation corresponds to $\phi_{CN} = 300° - 360°$, and the
syn-conformation to $\phi_{CN} = 120° - 180°$.   For the pyrimidine
nucleoside with C_2'-endo-sugar, three energetically favorable
ranges of the conformation occur at about $\phi_{CN} = 326°$ (anti),
$230° - 228°$, and $130° - 128°$ (syn).   The syn-conformation of
pyrimidines with C_2'-endo-sugar was predicted to be a little
more stable than the anti-conformation.   On the other hand,
for the pyrimidines with C_3'-endo-sugan, the anti-conformation
is stable than the syn-conformation by more than 20 kJ mol^{-1}.
The predicted conformation of cytidine with C_3'-endo-sugar is
in good agreement with the observed conformation of cytidine
in crystal[17] ($\phi_{CN} = 342°$).
     The CD and MCD obtained for cytidine predicted that the
lowest two transitions are characterized by the transitions
from the nonbonding orbitals of carbonyl oxygen and azanitrogen
to the unoccupied π^* orbitals.   And the third transition
corresponds to the lowest $\pi^*\leftarrow\pi$ transition of the cytidine
moiety, as assumed on the basis of the MCD results.   As many
electronic transitions are predicted in the higher wavenumber
region (above 42000 cm^{-1}), the MCD and CD spectra in this spectral region are difficult to be analyzed.   The calculated
rotational strengths are sensitive to the conformation of the
furanose ring and the sugar-base torsion angle, ϕ_{CN}, while the
calculated Faraday B terms are not much affcted by these structu-
ral parameters.   Thus, the MCD results afford us valuable
informations on the electronic states of the given nucleosides.
     The INDO-MO results calculated for isocytidine predicted
that the two electronic transitions of $\pi^*\leftarrow n$ appear below 35000
cm^{-1}.   However, any distinct MCD and CD bands are not observed in this spectral region.

The intense absorption band observed for 2,5'-O-cyclo-2',3'-O-isopropylidene uridine at 42000 cm^{-1} is resolved into two MCD bands, and this suggests that two independent electronic transitions are included in the lowest absorption.   Although the MCD spectrum of 2,2'-O-cyclouridine resembles to that of 2,5'-O-cyclo-2',3'-O-isopropylidene uridine, the CD signs of these compounds are opposite to each other.   The calculated CD signs of the two lowest $\pi^* \leftarrow \pi$ transitions are negative for 2,5'-O-cyclo-2'3'-O-isopropylidene uridine and positive for 2,2'-O-cyclouridine, which are in good agreement with the experimental results.   The large CD band observed in the higher wavenumber (45000 - 52000 cm^{-1}) is interpreted to be mainly originated from the $\pi^* \leftarrow n$ transition of the uridine moiety.   Furthermore, the MCD results of cytosine and isocytosine are discussed for the references.   The detailed experimental and theoretical results will be published elsewhere in near future.

REFERENCES

1. Voelter,W.,Records,E.,Bunnenberg,E., and Djerassi,C.(1968)J.Am.Chem.Soc. 90, 6163;Elder,D.L.,Bunnenberg,E.,Djerassi,C.,Ikehara,M., and Voelter, W.(1970) Tetrahedron Lett. 10, 727
2. Townsend,L.B.,Miles,D.W.,Manning,S.J., and Eyring,H.(1970)J.Heterocyclic Chem. 10, 419
3. Miles,D.W.,Inskeep,W.H.,Townsend,L.B., and Eyring,H.(1972)Biopolymers, 11, 1181
4. Weiler-Feilchenfeld,H.,Linder,R.E.,Barth,G.,Bunnenberg,E., and Djerassi, C.(1977)Theoret.Chim.Acta 46, 79
5. Kaito,A. and Hatano, M.(1980)Bull.Chem.Soc. in press.
6. Wallace,S.L.,Castellan,A.,Muller,D.,and Michl,J.(1978)J.Am.Chem.Soc. 100, 6828;Jonas,I. and Michl,J.(1978) 100, 6834
7. Miles,D.W.,Robins,M.J.,Robins,R.K.,Winkley,M.W., and Eyring,H.(1969)J. Am.Chem.Soc. 91, 824; Idem.(1969) ibid. 91, 831
8. Inskeep,W.H.,Miles,D.W. and Eyring,H.(1970)J.Am.Chem.Soc. 92, 3866
9. Miles,D.W.,Inskeep,W.H.,Robins,M.J.,Winkley,M.W.,Robins,R.K. and Eyring, H.(1970)J.Am.Chem.Soc. 92, 3872
10. Cushley,R.J.,Wempen,I. and Fox,J.J.(1968)J.Am.Chem.Soc. 90, 709
11. Holy,A.,Rogers,G.T. and Ulbricht,T.L.V.(1970)FEBS Lett. 7, 335;Rogers, G.T. and Ulbricht, T.L.V.(1970) ibid. 7, 337
12. Kaito,A.,Tajiri,A.,Hatano,M.,Ogura,F. and Nakagawa,M.(1976)J.Am.Chem. Soc. 98, 7932
13. Kaito,A.,Hatano,M. and Tajiri,A.(1977)J.Am.Chem.Soc. 99, 5241
14. Kaito,A. and Hatano,M.(1978)J.Am.Chem.Soc. 100, 2034
15. Kaito,A. and Hatano,M.(1978)J.Am.Chem.Soc. 100, 4037
16. Kaito,A. and Hatano,M.(1980)Bull.Chem.Soc.Japan, in press.
17. Furberg,S.,Petersen,C.S.,and Rømming,Chr.(1965)Acta Cryst. 18, 313
18. Prusiner,P.,Brennan,T. and Sundaralingam, M.(1973)Biochemistry 12, 1196
19. Manor,P.C., Saenger,W., Davies,D.B.,Jankowski,K. and Rabczenko,A.(1973) Biochim.Biophys.Acta 340, 472;Delbaere,L.T.J. and James, M.N.G.(1973) Acta Cryst. B29, 2905

Synthesis of stacked purine bases[1]

Fumio Hama, Yoshiteru Sakata and Soichi Misumi

The Institute of Scientific and Industrial Research, Osaka University, Yamadakami, Suita, Osaka 565, Japan

ABSTRACT

Two purine base layered compounds and the related compounds were synthesized. Chemical shifts of ^{1}H NMR and marked hypochromism in UV spectra demonstrate the two phanes to be layered structure.

INTRODUCTION

It is well known that nucleic acid bases are stacked parallel and partially with the interplanar distance of ca. 3.4 Å in the helical structure of DNA and the stacking brings about a significant hypochromic effect on electronic spectra, which was theoretically interpreted by Tinoco[2] and Rodes[3]. A number of model compounds, especially two bases bridged by a polymethylene chain, have been synthesized to study the relationship between structure and base-to-base interaction. In these model compounds, however, it was difficult to evaluate the hypochromic effect in detail owing to the conformational fluctuation of two base moieties in solution. We now report the first synthesis of purine bases stacked in cyclophane type, 1a and 1b, where two chromophores are closely fixed by two polymethylene chains.

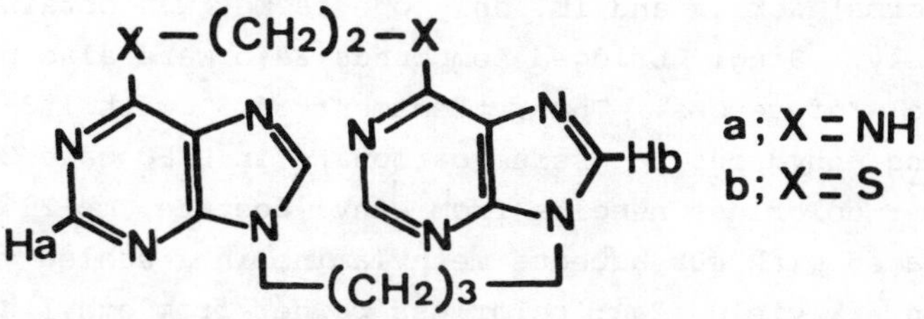

$$X - (CH_2)_2 - X$$

Ha · · · Hb

a; X = NH
b; X = S

$$(CH_2)_3$$

1a,b

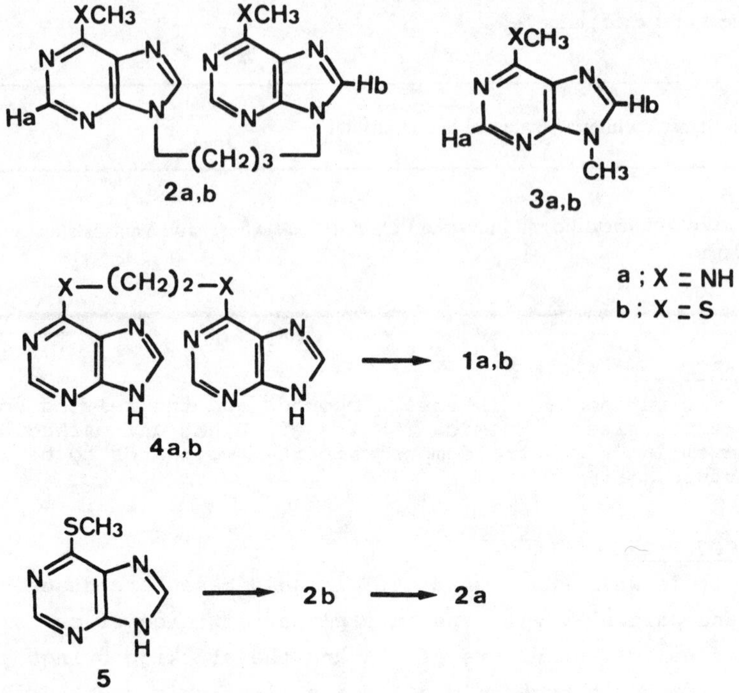

XCH3   XCH3
Ha   2a,b   Hb
—(CH2)3—

XCH3
Ha   3a,b   Hb
CH3

a ; X = NH
b ; X = S

X—(CH2)2—X

4a,b   ⟶   1a,b

SCH3

5   ⟶   2b   ⟶   2a

RESULTS

Cyclization of 4a[5] or 4b[6] to 1a or 1b, respectively was
achieved by treatment with 1,3-dibromopropane and sodium hydride
in DMF under dilution conditions. Crude product was purified by
chromatography on silica gel (Merk Kieselgel-60) with methanol
and following recrystallization (1a[7]: 4% yield, colorless plates
from benzene, dec. > 325°C ; 1b[7]: 2% yield, colorless plates from
toluene, dec. > 320°C). Of two possible isomers (eclipsed and
crossed forms) for 1a and 1b, only one isomer was obtained
respectively. Singly bridged compounds 2a,b were also prepared
as spectral references. Thus, treatment of 5[8] with 1,3-dibromo-
propane and anhydrous potassium carbonate in DMSO gave 2b in 47%
yield (2b[7]: colorless needles from ethyl acetate, mp 236-237°C).
2b was heated with 40% aqueous methylamine in a sealed tube to
give 2a in 68% yield (2a[7]: colorless powder from ethyl acetate,
mp 241-242°C).

Table Observed Chemical Shifts (δ, ppm in CDCl$_3$)
of Aromatic Protons of 1-3

	1a	2a	3a	1b	2b	3b
Ha	8.10	8.40	8.43	8.60	8.73	8.74
Hb	7.47	7.92	7.71	7.52	8.12	7.93

Chemical shifts of aromatic protons of 1, 2, and related
monomers 3a[9] and 3b[10] are summarized in Table. Upfield shifts
were observed for Ha and Hb of 1 as compared with the corresponding protons of 2 and 3, indicating the layered structure
of 1. However, the determination of isomeric form for both 1a
and 1b could not be made unequivocally.

Electronic spectra of 1-3 are shown in Figs. 1 and 2. It
is noticeable that 1a and 1b show remarkable hypochromic effect
even in methanol, because in the same solvent there is no stacking interaction for trimethylene bridged compounds 2a and 2b,
which have been hitherto considered to be a dimer model of
nucleic acid bases. This fact also supports the layered structure of 1a and 1b.

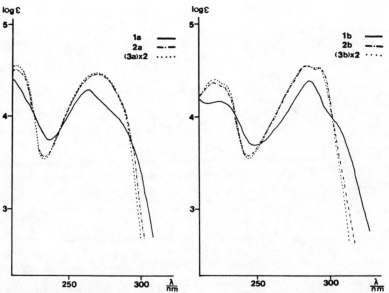

Fig. 1. Electronic spectra
of 1a-3a in ethanol.

Fig. 2. Electronic spectra
of 1b-3b in ethanol.

X-ray analysis of 1a and 1b is in progress for a quantitative treatment of the hypochromism.

REFERENCES

1. Layered Compounds. LXVI. Part LXV: Kaneda, T., Ogawa, T., Toyoda, T. and Misumi, S., submitted to Bull. Chem. Soc. Jpn.
2. Tinoco, Jr. I. (1960) J. Am. Chem. Soc. 82, 4785-4790
3. Rhodes, W. (1961) J. Am. Chem. Soc. 83, 3609-3617
4. Leonard, N. J. (1979) Acc. Chem. Res. 12, 423-429
5. Lister, J. H. (1960) J. Chem. Soc., 3682-3684
6. Lewis, L. R., Noell, C. W., Beaman, A. G. and Robins, R. K. (1962) J. Medicin. Pharm. Chem. 5, 607-617
7. Satisfactory elemental analysis and mass spectral data were obtained.
8. Elion, G. B., Burgi, E. and Hitchings, G. H. (1952) J. Am. Chem. Soc. 74, 411-414
9. Brown, D. J. and Ford, P. W. (1969) J. Chem. Soc.(C), 2620-2624
10. Brown, D. J. and Jacobsen, N. W. (1965) J. Chem. Soc., 3770-3778

Synthesis and interactions of poly-L-lysines containing nucleic acid bases

Yoshiaki Inaki, Tomohiro Ishikawa and Kiichi Takemoto

Department of Petroleum Chemistry, Faculty of Engineering, Osaka University, Suita, Osaka 565, Japan

ABSTRACT
    Poly-L-lysine derivatives containing nucleic acid bases were synthesized.   Conformation of the obtained polymers was studied by CD and ORD.   Formation of the polymer complex was studied and was related to the conformation of the polymers.

INTRODUCTION
    A series of nucleic acid analogs has been designed and pre-pared, and their functionalities have been estimated in relation to specific base-base pairing properties[1].   In these inves-tigation, however, it was difficult to know the conformation of the polymers in solution.   When poly-α-amino acid is used as the backbone chain, it is possible to know the secondary struc-ture of these synthetic polymers.
    In the present study, poly-L-lysine derivatives containing pendant nucleic acid bases were synthesized.   The conforma-tion and the interaction of these polymers were studied to see how the property and the structure of the backbone and the side chain influenced the formation of the polymer complex.

MATERIALS
    Following polymers were synthesized.
    Poly-L-lysine Derivatives:[2]

$$\{NH-CH-CO\}_{1-x} - \{NH-CH-CO\}_x$$
$$(CH_2)_4 \qquad (CH_2)_4$$
$$NH_2 \qquad NH-CO-CH_2CH_2-Base$$

Base: Ade (PLL-A-x)
      Thy (PLL-T-x)
      Ura (PLL-U-x)

Low molecular weight polymers were prepared by NCA method[3].

Poly(N-β-methacryloyloxyethyl) Derivatives: [4]

$$\begin{array}{l} \text{CH}_3 \\ \text{+CH}_2-\text{C+} \\ \text{CO-O-CH}_2\text{CH}_2\text{-Base} \end{array}$$

Base: Ade (polyMAOA)
      Thy (polyMAOT)

Poly(N-β-methacryloylaminoethyl) Derivatives: [5]

$$\begin{array}{l} \text{CH}_3 \\ \text{+CH}_2-\text{C+} \\ \text{CO-NH-CH}_2\text{CH}_2\text{-Base} \end{array}$$

Base: Ade (polyMAEA)
      Ura (polyMAEU)

RESULTS AND DISCUSSION

Conformation of the Poly-L-lysine Derivatives.

In acidic solution, CD spectra were measured.   From these spectra, the residue ellipticy at 222 nm are plotted against pH of the system in Figure 1.   Even at lower pH than 4, PLL-A-67 has partial helical conformation in spite of mutual repultion between the positively charged adenine bases.   With increasing pH of the system, helicity of the polymer increased by release from the electrostatic repulsion between the positively charged side chains.   Above pH 2.5, as the polymer bagan to precipitate from the aqueous solution, the spectra could not be measured.   Poly-L-lysine, however, existed in random coil structure in acidic aqueous solution.

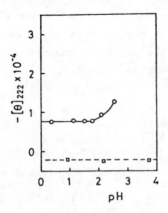

Fig. 1. $-[\theta]_{222}$ vs. pH.
PLL-A-67 (O), PLL (□).

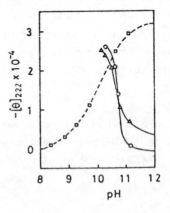

Fig. 2. $-[\theta]_{222}$ vs. pH.
PLL-T-93 (O), PLL-T-79 (△),
PLL (□).

In Figure 2, the values $-[\theta]_{222}$ for PLL-T-93 and PLL-T-79 are plotted against pH of the system in the alkaline pH region. These polymers tend to exist in helical conformation at neutral pH, while PLL exists in random coil structure due to electrostatic repulsion. Decrease of helicity at high pH may be caused by the repulsion between the negatively charged thymine bases.

A similar tendency was found in the case of PLL-U-93 and PLL-U-76 (Figure 3).

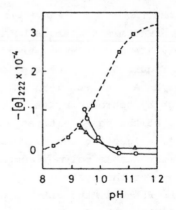

Fig. 3. $-[\theta]_{222}$ vs. pH. PLL-U-93(○), PLL-U-76(△), PLL(□).

Interaction between PLL-A and PLL-T.

The interaction between PLL-A-53 and PLL-T-97 was clearly observed in DMSO-EG (3/2, v/v) as shown in Figure 4. The complex formation was found to be influenced by solvents, time, temperature and contents of nucleic acid bases in the polymer.

From the ORD data, the helicity of the polymer was found to depend on the nucleic acid base content and degree of polymerization. It can be concluded that the decrease of helical structure causes the decrease of interaction with the polymers containing the complementary nucleic acid bases.

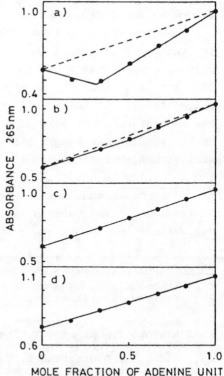

Fig. 4. Mixing curves between PLL-A-67 and PLL-T-x.
x: a) 93, b) 79, c) 65, and d) 100, low. mol. wt..

Interaction with MAO-type Polymers.

The mixing curves between polyMAOA and PLL-T-x are shown in Figure 5. The system of polyMAOA with PLL-T-93 shows high hypochromicity value of 53% at the base unit ratio of 1:1, suggesting the formation of the stable polymer complex.

For the systems of polyMAOA with PLL-U-x, and PLL-A-x with polyMAOT, the formation of the polymer complex was also observed.

Interaction with MAE-type Polymers.

The ability of polyMAE-type derivatives for forming the polymer complex was found to be higher than that of the MAO-type polymers. The MAE-type polymer can interact not only with the high molecular weight PLL derivatives, but also with the low molecular weight PLL derivatives.

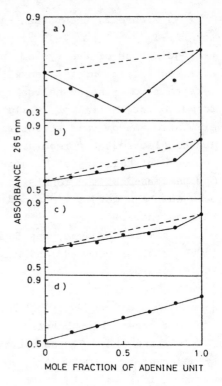

Fig. 5. Mixing curves between polyMAOA and PLL-T-x.
x: a) 93, b) 79, c) 65, and d) 100, low. mol. wt..

It appears that the MAE-type polymers having amide groups in the side chains tend to mix readily with the poly-L-lysine derivatives to promote the polymer complex formation.

REFERENCES

1 K. Takemoto, *J. Polymer Sci. Polymer Symposia,* 55, 105 (1976).
2 T. Ishikawa, Y. Inaki and K. Takemoto, *Polymer Bulletin,* 1, 85 (1978).
3 T. Ishikawa, Y. Inaki and K. Takemoto, *ibid.,* 1, 215 (1978).
4 M. Akashi, T. Okimoto, Y. Inaki and K. Takemoto, *J. Polymer Sci. Polymer Chem. Ed.,* 17, 905 (1979).
5 Y. Inaki, S. Sugita and K. Takemoto, *J. Polymer Sci. Polymer Chem. Ed.,* submitted for publication.

Nucleic Acids Research

Structure and stability of complexes between poly-5-bromouridylic acid and 2,9-dimethyladenine or 2-methyladenosine

Shigesada Higuchi and Kumiko Yasui

Mitsubishi- Kasei Institute of Life Sciences, Machida, Tokyo 194, Japan

ABSTRACT

The complexes formed between poly-5-bromouridylic acid (poly(BU)) and 2,9-dimethyladenine (m^2m^9A) or 2-methyladenosine (m^2Ado) were investigated. The stoichiometry of the m^2m^9A-poly (BU) complex was found to be 1:1 as determined by equilibrium dialysis measurements. The CD spectra of the complexes showed the formation of helically ordered structure. This is also confirmed by the sharp melting profiles. A comparison of the CD spectra with that of poly(m^2A)·poly(BU) complex revealed a close relationship of the helical structures for these three types of complexes. It was observed that the m^2m^9A was able to form a thermally more stable complex with the poly(BU) than the m^2Ado did.

INTRODUCTION

A variety of modified purine nucleosides was found to locate at the position adjacent to the 3'-side of the anticodon of some specific tRNAs. 2-Methyladenosine, one of such nucleosides, is known to appear in the tRNAs with the anticodon starting with G or C. In order to understand the biological roles of the m^2Ado in the architecture of tRNA molecule, it is significant to know precisely its properties in the monomeric state, since in general the modified nucleosides appear as scattered spots. We have already reported that the association of the 2-methyl-9-n-propyl-adenine to 1-cyclohexyluracil was of the same order as that of 9-n-propyladenine to 1-cyclohexyluracil in $CDCl_3$ in which the isolated planer base-pair was formed through hydrogen bonding[1]. In this communication, we describe the formation and the charac-teristic properties of the helical complexes between the poly(BU) and m^2Ado or m^2m^9A in aqueous solution.

MATERIALS AND METHODS

The m^2m^9A was synthesized from 2-methyladenine (Sigma) and the poly(BU) was prepared as described. The m^2Ado was kindly provided by Dr. M. Yamazaki and Dr. M. Hattori. The equilibrium dialysis experiments were done with a Kontron diapack system, and the CD spectra and thermal melting were measured with a Jasco J-40 and a Gilford 2400S respectively.

RESULTS AND DISCUSSION

Figure 1 shows a binding isotherm for the formation of the m^2m^9A-poly(BU) complex which was constructed on the basis of the equilibrium dialysis measurements. The stoichiometry of the complex was determined to be 1:1 unequivocally. It is seen from Figure 1 that the formation of the complex occurs very abruptly. Namely, the transition is in a remarkably narrow range of the monomer concentration. This reflects that the interaction energy of the complex is appreciably large in contrast to the complex formed with the poly(U)[2]. Similar results were obtained for the interacting system in which the poly(BU) participated[3]. However, low thermal stability of the m^2Ado-poly(BU) complex did not permit us to carry out the equilibrium dialysis experiments.

Figure 2 shows the CD spectra of the m^2m^9A-poly(BU) complex and the m^2Ado-poly(BU) complex. Both spectra illustrate their helical character definitely, suggesting also the structure of both complexes are closely related each other, while either CD

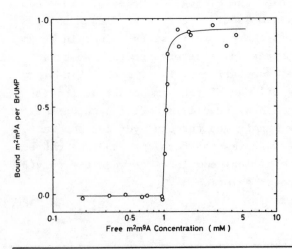

Figure 1. A binding isotherm for the formation of m^2m^9A-poly(BU) complex at 4°C, in 0.4 M NaCl-0.02 M Na-cacodylate-10^{-4} M EDTA (pH 7.0); poly(BU), 1.2×10^{-3} M.

spectrum is entirely different from the one obtained by adding respective component spectra.

Thus, the structure of the complexes should be double helical with the Hoogsteen type base-pairing, because the presence of a substituent at the position 2 would restrain to form the Watson-Crick type base-pairing. Features of the CD spectra of the m^2Ado-poly(BU) complex are quite similar to those of poly(m^2A)·poly(BU) complex[4] and it seems possible to interpret the CD spectra of these three types of complexes in terms of the same or a very similar conformation around the base-pairs. It is pointed out that the adenine base and its analogues possess inherent

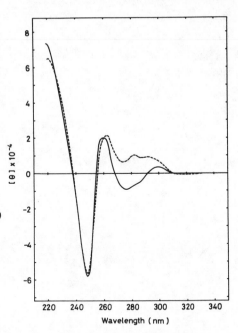

Figure 2. CD spectra of the m^2m^9A-poly(BU) complex (———) and the m^2Ado-poly(BU) complex (-----) in 0.4 M NaCl-0.02 M Na-cacodylate -10^{-4} M EDTA (pH 7.0) below 0°C.

properties to build up the helical structure by directing the conformation of poly(BU) through forming the hydrogen bondings and the orderly self-stackings.

The thermal stability of the complexes were compared each other under the same conditions. It was observed that the m^2m^9A (in which a methyl residue replaced the ribose) could form a more stable complex with the poly(BU) than the m^2Ado did. This is explained as a steric effect that the bulky ribose which does not take part in the back bone structure is lacking in the former case. An attempt to evaluate the thermodynamic parameter from dependence of the melting temperatures on the monomer concentration is now in progress.

REFERENCES
1 Higuchi, S. and Dezaki, Y. (1977) Chemistry Letters 683-688.
2 Davies, R.J.H. and Davidson, N. (1971) Biopolymers 10, 1455-1479.
3 Higuchi, S. and Yasui, K. unpublished results.
4 a personal communication from Dr. M. Hattori.

Interactions between oligonucleotides having a left-handed helical structure and ethidium bromide

Seiichi Uesugi, Toshio Shida, Akira Miyamae and Morio Ikehara

Faculty of Pharmaceutical Sciences, Osaka University, Suita, Osaka 565, Japan

ABSTRACTS

Oligonucleotides containing 8,2'-S-cycloadenosine(A^S), 8,2'-S-cycloinosine(I^S), 6,2'-O-cyclouridine(U^o) and 6,2'-O-cyclocytidine(C^o) residues, which have a glycosidic torsion angle(χ) of about 120°, were synthesized. Among these oligomers, $A^S pU^o$, $A^S pI^S$ and $(pC^o)_4$ + $(pI^S)_4$ formed a complex with ethidium bromide, which was assumed to be intercalated between the adjacent base-pairs of the left-handed double helix.

INTRODUCTION

We have been studying on the oligonucleotides containing cyclonucleoside residues to elucidate the effects of the glyco-

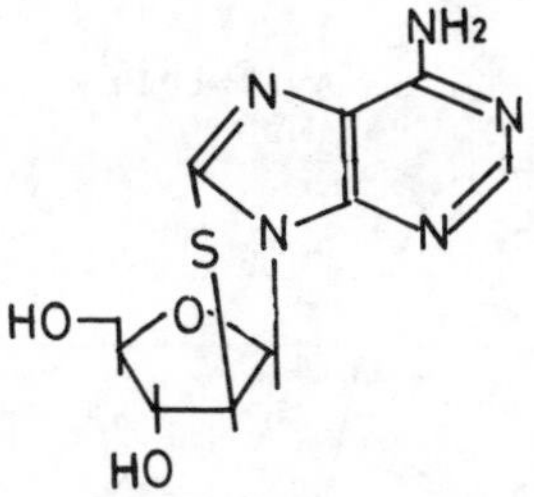

A^S 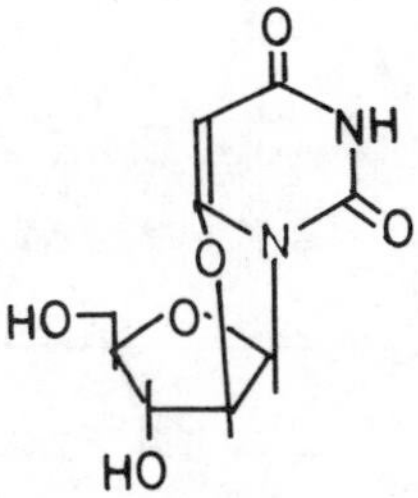 U^o 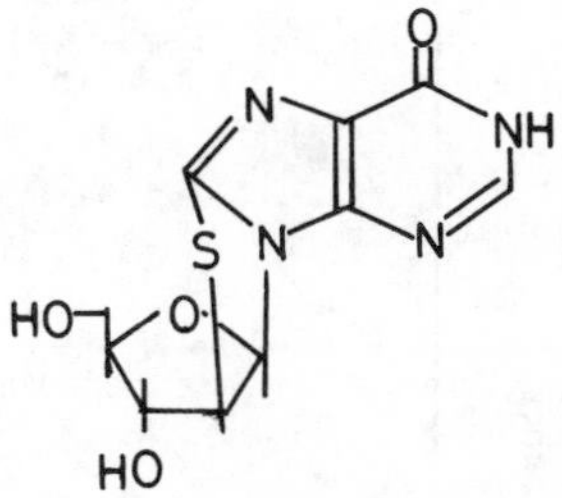 I^S

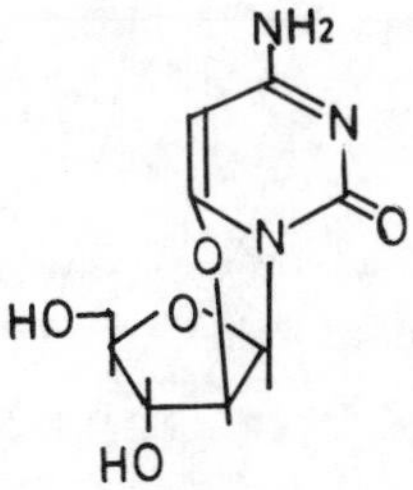

C^o 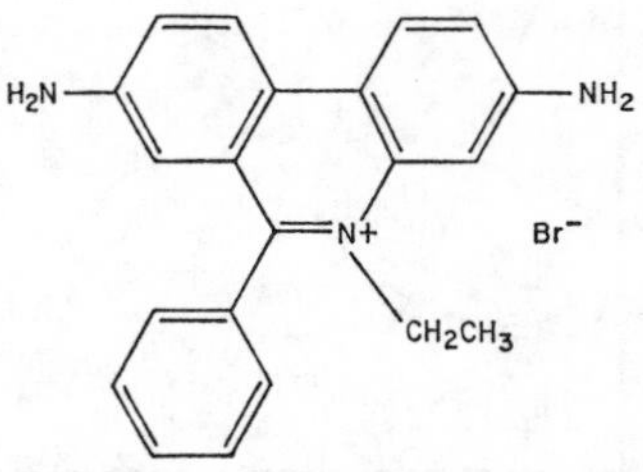   ethidium bromide

sidic torsion angles on oligonucleotide conformation.[1,2] It was
found that the oligonucleotides containing cyclonucleosides hav-
ing a high <u>anti</u>($\chi \approx 120°$) glycosidic torsion angle have a tendency
to take a left-handed helical structure. Recently we synthesized
self-complementary dinucleotides, A^SpU^{o2}, $U^{o}pA^{S2}$, A^SpI^S and I^SpA^S,
and homooligonucleotides, $(pC^{o})_n$ and $(pI^S)_n$. All the cyclonucleoside residues here (structures shown in the previous page) have
a high <u>anti</u> glycosidic torsion angle. In this paper, we report
interactions between these oligonucleotides and ethidium bromide
. Ethidium bromide is known to bind specifically to double heli-
ce of DNA and RNA. The planar phenanthridinium ring intercala-
tes between adjacent base-pairs of the double-helix.[3] It is also
known to stabilize base pairing between dinucleoside monophosphates by intercalation.[4]

MATERIALS AND METHODS
    A^SpI^S was synthesized by condensation of N,N,5'-<u>O</u>-tribenzoy-

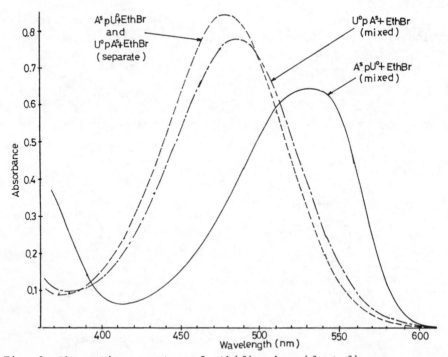

Fig. 1. Absorption spectra of ethidium bromide + dimers.

1-A^{s}p and 3'-O-Benzoyl-
I^s. I^{s}pA^s was synthesized by condensation of
5'-O-monomethoxytrityl-
I^s and N,N,3'-O-triben-
zoyl-pA^s. (pC°)$_n$ was synthesized by polymeriza-
tion of N-benzoyl-pC°-N-
benzoyl 2'-O-acetyl-pC°
mixture. (pI^s)$_n$ was synthesized by deamination
of (pA^s)$_n$. Absorption
spectra were recorded on
a Hitachi 200-10 spectro-
photometer. Circular di-
chroism(CD) spectra were
recorded on a JASCO ORD/
UV-5 spectropolarimeter.

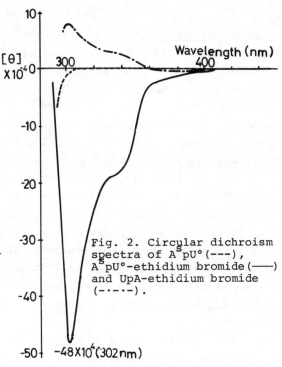

Fig. 2. Circular dichroism
spectra of A^{s}pU°(---),
A^{s}pU°-ethidium bromide(——)
and UpA-ethidium bromide
(-·-·-·-).

RESULTS AND DISCUSSION
1. Conformational properties of the oligomers

Two sets of the self-complementary dimers show similar trend
in conformational stability as judged by ^{1}H-NMR, CD and absorption studies. The dimer containing 5'-linked A^s residue (U°pA^s or
I^{s}pA^s) takes a left-handed stacked conformation more stable than
that of the corresponding counterpart (A^{s}pU° or A^{s}pI^s). It may be
due to the stronger base stacking involving the pyrimidine part
of the adenine ring. The oligomers of pI^s take a left-handed conformation similar to but weaker than that of (pA^s)$_n$[5]. The oligomers of pC° do not take a stacked conformation at all as judged
from the CD and ^{1}H-NMR data.
2. Interactions with ethidium bromide observed by absorption stu-
dies.

Absorption spectra in a visible region were recorded before
and after mixing the appropriate solutions in a split compartme-
nt cell. The results for A^{s}pU° and U°pA^s(1.5x10^{-3}M) at 0°C are
shown in Fig. 1. The ethidium bromide (1.5x10^{-4}M) solution exhibits dramatically different spectral properties after mixing

with A^spU°. On the other hand the ethidium bromide-$U^\circ pA^s$ solution does not exhibit these characteristics. Similar phenomena were observed also in the case of A^spI^s and I^spA^s, the former showing a dramatic change. Similar observation has been reported in the case of natural ApU and UpA, the latter showing a profound change[4]. These results clearly indicate that ethidium bromide binds to A^spU°, A^spI^s and UpA specifically with respect to the corresponding sequence isomers, $U^\circ pA^s$, I^spA^s and ApU.

3. CD spectra of the ethidium bromide-oligomer complexes

The ethidium bromide-A^spU° complex showed large negative CD bands in 300-400 nm region as shown in Fig. 2. These bands must be induced by interactions of the phenanthridinium ring of ethidium bromide with the bases of the dimer because ethidium bromide itself has no optical activity. In the case of UpA-ethidium bromide complex, relatively small positive bands are observed (shown also in Fig.2)[4]. The ethidium bromide-A^spI^s complex also showed negative CD bands with similar pattern but greater magnitudes when compared with those for the A^spU° complex. Upon addition of ethidium bromide to a mixture of $(pC^\circ)_4$ and $(pI^s)_4$(1:1), similar induced CD bands were observed though the magnitudes were far smaller.

4. Temperature effect on the complex

Thermal melting behavior of the ethidium bromide-oligomer complex was examined by absorption and CD studies. Both analyses for the ethidium bromide-A^spU° complex showed relatively sharp transition at 9°C. This result suggests that the complex melts cooperatively and therefore, involves base pairing between two molecules of A^spU°.

REFERENCES
1. Uesugi, S., Yano, J., Yano, E. and Ikehara, M. (1977)J. Am. Chem. Soc. 99, 2313-2323 and references therein.
2. Ikehara, M., Uesugi, S. and Shida, T. (1980) Chem. Pharm. Bull . 28, 189-197
3. Tsai, C.C., Jain, S.C. and Sobell, H.M. (1977) J. Mol. Biol. 114, 301-315
4. Krugh, T.R. and Reinhardt, C.G.(1975)J. Mol. Biol.97,133-162
5. Ikehara, M. and Uesugi, S.(1972)J.Am.Chem.Soc.94,9189-9193

Symposium Series No.8 1980

Nucleic Acids Research

^{13}C-NMR studies on tertiary structures of E. coli tRNAs with ^{13}C-labeling method

Shigeyuki Yokoyama, Kazue M.J.Usuki and Tatsuo Miyazawa
Department of Biophysics and Biochemistry, Faculty of Science, University of Tokyo, Hongo, Bunkyo-ku, Tokyo 113, and

Ziro Yamaizumi and Susumu Nishimura
Biology Division, National Cancer Center Research Institute, Tsukiji, Chou-ku, Tokyo 104, Japan

INTRODUCTION

Modified nucleosides located in specific positions of tRNAs are important in the functions of tRNAs in protein biosynthesis. The NMR signals of these modified nucleosides will be good probes in the NMR studies on tertiary structures of tRNAs interacting with aminoacyl tRNA synthetases, polypeptide chain elongation factor Tu, *etc*. Recently, Agris *et al*. measured ^{13}C-NMR spectra of unfractionated tRNA with ^{13}C-labeling of modified nucleosides.[1-3] In the present study, we fractionated ^{13}C-labeled tRNAs and compared the tertiary structures of these tRNAs by the analysis of ^{13}C-NMR spectra.

MATERIALS AND METHODS

E. coli rel⁻met⁻ strain was grown in a medium containing ^{13}C-methyl methionine, and tRNA was extracted by Zubay's method. By several chromatographies, fractions containing one or two tRNA species were prepared. 67.9-MHz ^{13}C-NMR spectra were measured of these tRNAs with $MgCl_2$(10mM) and NaCl(100mM).

RESULTS AND DISCUSSION

Two or more prominent signals were observed in the high-field region of each ^{13}C-NMR spectrum. Compared with the primary structures of tRNAs, these signals were unambiguously assigned to methyl (or methylene) carbons of ribothymidine, 5-methylaminomethyl-2-thiouridine, uridine-5-oxyacetic acid, 6-methyladenosine, 2-methyladenosine, 7-methylguanosine, *etc*.

For various tRNAs, the chemical shifts of signals assigned to a common modified nucleoside are nearly equal, indicating that the tertiary structures around functionally important modified nucleosides are similar among tRNAs. The chemical shifts of these signals depend appreciably on pH. Thus, tertiary structures of tRNAs may be studied in detail by ^{13}C-NMR spectroscopy on ^{13}C-labeled molecules.

REFERENCES

1. Agris, P. F., Fujiwara, F. G., Schmidt, C. F. and Loeppky, R. N. (1975) *Nucleic Acids Research 2*, 1503-1512.
2. Tompson, J. G., Hayashi, F., Paukstelis, J. V., Loeppky, R. N. and Agris, P. F. (1979) *Biochemistry 18*, 2079-2085.
3. Tompson, J. G. and Agris, P. F. (1979) *Nucleic Acids Research 7*, 765-779.

Nucleic Acids Research

Dinucleoside monophosphate having a high anti conformation. II. The crystal structure of 8,2'-S-cycloinosinyl-(3',5')-8,2'-S-cycloadenosine hexahydrate

Kensaku Hamada, Yoshiko Matsuo, Akira Miyamae, Satoshi Fujii and Ken-ichi Tomita

Faculty of Pharmaceutical Sciences, Osaka University, Yamada-kami, Suita, Osaka 565, Japan

ABSTRACT

The crystal and molecular structure of 8,2'-S-cycloinosinyl-(3',5')-8,2'-S-cycloadenosine (I^SpA^S) hexahydrate has been determined by X-ray diffraction method. The torsion angles around the sugar-phosphate backbone are unique and different from those found in the crystalline dinucleoside monophosphates so far determined; The rotation around the P-O bond, (ω',ω), is (g^+,t). An I^SpA^S molecule is in a folded form. There is no intramolecular base stacking or base-pairing but the intermolecular base stacking is dominant.

INTRODUCTION

The glycosidic torsion angle X of 8,2'-S-cyclopurine nucleosides is fixed in a high anti region ($X=100°\sim120°$) and the dinucleoside monophosphates having this unusual X-value should show the drastic changes in their molecular conformations, i.e., the left-handed stacking is proposed from the CD spectra[1] and the energy calculations.[2]

We had reported the crystal and molecular structure of 8,2'-S-cycloadenosine dimer (A^SpA^S) at the preceding meeting.[3] The obtained conformation did not present the left-handed stacked form. Therefore, as the next compound, we have synthesized I^SpA^S, which is capable to form a self-complementary base-pairing, and here report its crystal and molecular structure determined by X-ray diffraction method.

METHOD

I^SpA^S was synthesized by condensation of 8,2'-S-cycloinosine and 8,2'-S-cycloadenosine 5'-monophosphate, which were previously obtained by cyclization reaction of adenosine and adenosine

5'-monophosphate[4] with dicyclohexyl carbodiimide. Prismatic
transparent crystals were obtained by slow evaporation of an
aqueous solution of $I^S pA^S$. The chemical structure is shown in
Fig. 1 and the crystal data in Table 1. A total of 2,697 inde-
pendent intensity data within $\sin\theta/\lambda = 0.588\text{Å}^{-1}$ were collected on a
Rigaku automatic four-circle diffractomater with graphate-mono-
chromatized Cu-Kα radiation. The structure was solved by the
direct method using a program MULTAN 78[5] and refined by both full
matrix and block-diagonal least-squares methods. The final R
value is 0.065.

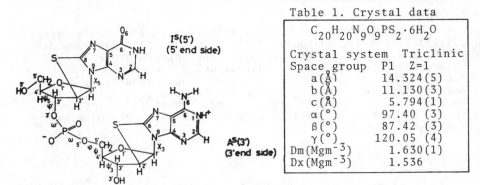

Table 1. Crystal data

$C_{20}H_{20}N_9O_9PS_2 \cdot 6H_2O$	
Crystal system	Triclinic
Space group P1	Z=1
a(Å)	14.324(5)
b(Å)	11.130(3)
c(Å)	5.794(1)
α(°)	97.40 (3)
β(°)	87.42 (3)
γ(°)	120.05 (4)
Dm(Mgm^{-3})	1.630(1)
Dx(Mgm^{-3})	1.536

Fig. 1. Chemical structure of $I^S pA^S$

RESULTS AND DISCUSSION

The conformation of $I^S pA^S$ molecule is shown in Fig. 2. As
shown in Fig. 1, the N(1) atom of the adenine base is protonated
due to the dissociation of phosphate group. The bond distances
and angles in the hypoxanthine and the protonated adenine bases
are similar to those in related compounds. However, the cyclization between the 8-position of the purine and the 2'-position
of the sugar ring causes the significant distortion in the sugar
moieties.

The conformational parameters are summarized in Table 2 with
those of $A^S pA^S$. The glycosidic torsion angles (X) are 125° (I^S)
and 127° (A^S) which are both in the high anti region. The sugar
puckering at 5'-end site (inosine site) is C(4')-endo, while this
at 3'-end site (adenosine site) is C(3')-endo. The latter
puckering is the first case for the cyclonucleosides, cyclo-

nucleotides and A^SpA^S fused at the 2'-position of the sugar ring. Some of the torsion angles related to sugar-phosphate backbone are quite different from those of dinucleoside monophosphates so far determined by X-ray diffraction method. Especially, two tor-sion angles (ω',ω) are 89° and 181°, respectively, representing (g^+,t) conformation which is quite different from (g^-,t) found in A^SpA^S or (g^-,g^-) frequently found in the other crystalline di-nucleoside monophosphates. As shown in Fig. 2, the hypoxanthine and adenine base planes are almost parallel with a twist angle of 3.1° and a distance of about 6.8Å. The overall molecular confor-mation is neither an extended form nor a helical form but it belongs to a folded form.

It is interesting to note that this folded conformatiom is not found in tRNA^{phe}[6] or oligonucleotides. There is no intermole-cular base-pairing, but the strong intermolecular base stacking with a distance of about 3.44Å and dihedral angle of about 3.1° was found. The distance between N(7) atom of the hypoxanthine base and N(6) atom of the adenine base of the adjacent molecule, 3.00Å, indicates the exsistance of the intermolecular hydrogen bond. Six water molecules participate in extensive hydrogen bond formation.

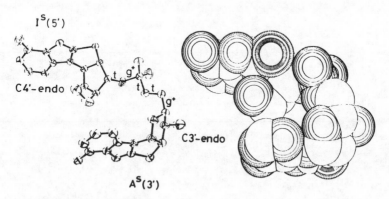

Fig. 2. Molecular structure of I^SpA^S. The left figure is illustrated by thermal ellipsoids and the right is shown by van der waals view.

Table 2. Torsion angle(°) for I^SpA^S and A^SpA^S

compounds		χ	ψ	ψ'	ϕ'	ω'	ω	ϕ
I^SpA^S	$I^Sp(5')$	125	72	135	211	89	---	---
	$pA^S(3')$	127	62	81	---	---	181	187
A^SpA^S -1	$A^Sp(5')$	117	57	140	209	301	---	---
	$pA^S(3')$	96	177	150	---	---	172	166
A^SpA^S -2	$A^Sp(5')$	117	57	141	210	304	---	---
	$pA^S(3')$	101	181	147	---	---	174	163

REFERENCE

1 Uesugi,S.,Yamamoto,M.,Ikehara,M.,Fang,K.N.and Ts'o,P.O.P.
   (1972)J.Amer.Chem.Soc.,94,5480-5486.
2 Fujii,S.and Tomita,K.(1976)Nucleic Acids Res.,3,1973-1984.
3 Fujii,S.,Miura,R.,Tomita,K.,Uesugi,S.and Ikehara,M.(1979)
   Nucleic Acids Symposium Series No.6,s69-s72.
4 Ikehara,M.and Uesugi,S.(1972)Tetrahedron,28,3687-3694.
5 Main,P.,Hull,S.E.,Lessinger,L.,Germain,D.,Declercq,J-P.and
   Woolfson,M.M.(1978) A System of Computer Programs for the
   Automatic Solution of Crystal Structures from X-ray Diffraction Data,MULTAN 78,University of York.
6 Jack,A.,Ladnae,J.E.and Klug,A.(1976) J.Mol.Biol.,108,619-649.

Inhibition by 2- or/and 8-substituted adenosine derivatives of adenosine deaminase and calmodulin-dependent phosphodiesterase

Yasuharu Sasaki and Yasutaka Ono

Biochemical Research Center, Foodstuff Plant, Asahi Chemical Ind. Co., Ltd., Asahi-machi 6-2700, Nobeoka 883, Miyazaki, Japan

ABSTRACT

Several 2- or/and 8-substituted adenosine derivatives were tested for their ability to inhibit the adenosine deaminase activity in hog heart and Ca^{++}, calmodulin-dependent phosphodiesterase activity in hog brain. Among these derivatives, 2-piperidyladenosine competitively inhibited not only the adenosine deaminase activity but also the phosphodiesterase activity. Further substitution of this compound with a bulky group at 8-position, 2-piperidyl-8-(8-aminooctylamino)-adenosine, abolished its ability to inhibit the adenosine deaminase activity, but progressively increased in the ability to inhibit the phosphodiasterase activity. On the other hand, 8-monosubstituted adenosine derivatives did not inhibit the adenosine deaminase activity.

INTRODUCTION

It is well known that cyclic AMP levels in many cell types can be modified by low concentrations of adenosine, perhaps this adenosine effect may be an action through adenosine receptor, purinergic site, coupled with adenylate cyclase. This effect is obserbed in brain slice (1), platelet (2), ventricular myocardium (3), and cultured cell (4,5). The extracellular levels of adenosine may be controlled by metabolic enzymes such as adenosine deaminase. Daly has reported that adenosine deaminase reduces extracellular levels of adenosine in brain tissue and thereby reduces the magnitude of accumulation of cyclic AMP elicited by biogenic amines (6), moreover certain phosphodiesterase inhibitors potentiate the adenosine effect. Therefore, we have synthesized adenosine derivatives and evaluated their inhibitory potentials to adenosine deaminase and phosphodiesterase activities.

MATERIALS and METHODS

Adenosine deaminase was partially purified from a supernatant of hog heart, through the procedues of 50-70 % $(NH_4)_2SO_4$ precipitation, DEAE-Sephadex column chromatography, and Sephadex G-100 gel filteration. Two peaks of the activity were appeared in the gel filteration, and the fractions of the second and major peak were pooled and used as enzyme preparation.

Calmodulin, a calcium binding protein, and its deficient cyclic nucleotide phosphodiesterase were prepared by the methods as described previously (7). 8-(8-aminooctylamino)-adenosine (CK-8), and 8-octylaminoadenosine were synthesized from 8-bromoadenosine and their corresponding alkylamines according to the methods with a minor modification described in previous paper (8). 2-Piperidyladenosine (2-Pip-Ado) was synthesized from 2-chloroadenosine and piperidine, and 2-piperidyl-8-(8-aminooctylamino)-adenosine (2-Pip-CK-8)from 2-piperidyl-8-bromoadenosine and 8-aminooctylamine. Details on these will be reported elsewhere. Other adenosine derivatives were synthesized by the methods as described previously (7,8).

RESULTS and DISCCUSION

A number of purine-modified adenosine derivatives, such as N^6-methyladenosine, N^6-phenyladenosine, 2-aminoadenosine, and 2-chloroadenosine, have been found to mimic the adenosine effect (3), and some derivatives are potent inhibitor of adenosine deaminase (9). We examined the inhibitory effect of 2-substituted adenosine on the activity of adenosine deaminase.

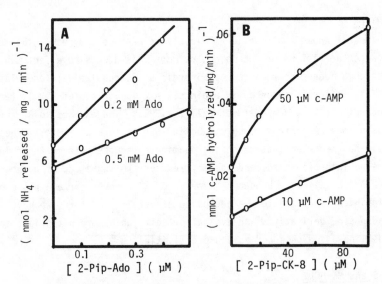

Fig.1   Inhibitory Effect of Adenosine Derivatives on Adenosine Deaminase Activity (A), and on Calmodulin-dependent Phosphodiesterase Activity (B).

Ado ; adenosine, c-AMP ; adenosine-3',5'-monophosphate.

As shown in Fig.1-A, 2-Pip-Ado competitively inhibited the adenosine deaminase activity in the preparation from hog brain heart. Moreover, this compound exhibited resistancy to the deaminase (data not shown). Other 2-sub-
stituted adenosine derivatives were evaluated (Table I). The intensity of
inhibitory potential of these derivatives was similar to one another.
While, of adenosine deaminase in calf intestinal mucosa (purchased from Sigma
), 2-Pip-Ado was a specific inhibitor, but other two compounds slightly inhibited it. The difference in inhibitory mode of derivatives suggests the organ
specificity of adenosine deaminase.

On the other hand, 2-Pip-Ado competitively inhibited the cyclic AMP hydrol-
yzing activity of Ca^{++},calmodulin-dependent phosphodiesterase. Further substitution of this compound with a bulky group at 8-position, 2-Pip-CK-8, increased in the inhibitory effect of derivative on the phosphodiesterase activity
, but abolished that on adenosine deaminase activity (Fig. 1-B).

Table I: Apparent Ki values for adenosine deaminase and phosphodiesterase
of adenosine derivatives

| | Substituent | | Adenosine Deaminase (μM) | | Phosphodiasterase |
	R_1	R_2	Hog Heart	Calf Int. Muc.*	(μM)
Adenosine	H	H	62 (Km)	86 (Km)	3000
2-Pip-Ado	C_5H_5N	H	140	40	870
2-Cl-Ado	Cl	H	120	530	NI**
2-NH_2-Ado	NH_2	H	130	720	NI
2-Pip-CK-8	C_5H_5N	$NH_2(CH_2)_8NH$	NI	NI	15
CK-8	H	$NH_2(CH_2)_8NH$	NI	NI	55
8-C_8S-Ado	H	$CH_3(CH_2)_7S$	NI	NI	12

*: the preparation from calf intestinal mucosa purchased from Sigma Co.

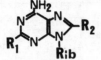

**; no inhibition.

We have reported that 8-substituted adenosine derivative with a long carbon
chain, which exhibits a large magnitude of negative Cotton effect in CD, inhibits the phosphodiesterase activity (7).
Fig.2 shows that a magnitude of negative Cotton effect of 8-substituted adenosine derivative increases according to the elongation of substituent.

The magnitude value of derivative with a substituent longer than n-butylthio group reaches a constant value, suggesting that the adenosine derivative having long carbon chain at 8-position takes syn conformation in neutral solution. These findings support the conception that 2-Pip-CK-8 may take syn conformation in neutral solution.

In conclusion, as one explanation of the lack of an ability of 2-Pip-CK-8 or 8-monosubstituted derivative to inhibit the adenosine deaminase activity, one may be able to propose *syn* conformation of derivative; the active site of the deaminase may be incapable of accepting the syn conformation of purine riboside. However, this hypothesis requires further investgations.

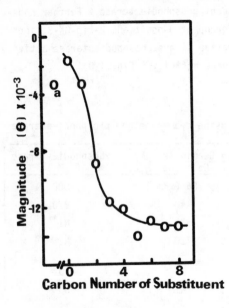

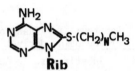

Fig.2. Relationship Between the Magnitude of Cotton Effect and the Carbon Number of Substituent of Derivatives.

a; adenosine. The carbon number correspondes to the methyl and methylene number of substituent at 8-position. The carbon number zero indicates 8-HS-adenosine.

REFERENCE
1. Sattin, A. and Rall, T.W. (1970) Mol. Pharmacol., 6: 13-23.
2. Haslam,R.J., and Rosson,G.M.(1975) Mol. Pharmacol.,11: 528-544.
3. Huang,M., and Drummond,G.I.(1976) Biochem. Pharmacol.,25: 2713-2719.
4. Clark,R.B., Gross,R., Su,Y.F., and Perkins,J.P.(1974) J. Biol. Chem., 249: 5296-5303.
5. Wolff,J., and Cook,G.H.(1977) J. Biol. Chem., 252: 687-693.
6. Daly,J.W.(1979) in Physiological and Regulatory Functions of Adenosine and Adenine Nucleotides, pp. 229-241.
7. Sasaki,Y., Kodaira,R., Nozawa,R., Yokota,T.,(1978) Biochem. Biophys. Res. Commun. 84: 277-284.
8. Sasaki,Y., Suzuki,N., Sowa,T., Nozawa,R., Yokota,T. (1976) Biochemistry 15: 1408-1413.
9. Ronca,G., and Zucchelli,G.(1968) Biochem. Biophys. Acta 159: 203-205.

Increased formation of 5-fluoro-2'-deoxyuridine 5'-monophosphate from 5-fluorouracil in the presence of a 2-deoxy-α-D-ribose 1-phosphate and 2'-deoxyuridine in Ehrlich ascites tumor cells

Osamu Tamemasa and Masakatsu Tezuka

Laboratory of Radiobiochemistry, Shizuoka College of Pharmacy, Oshika 2-2-1, Shizuoka-shi, 442, Japan

ABSTRACT

In expectation of the elevated formation of an antineoplastic metabolite from 5-fluorouracil (5FU), we examined the additive effect of 2-deoxy-α-D-ribose 1-phosphate (dRiblP) and/or 2'-deoxyuridine (dUrd) upon the formation of 5-fluoro-2'-deoxyuridine (5FdUrd) or proximately more antineoplastic 5-fluoro-2'-deoxyuridine 5'-monophosphate (5FdUMP) from 5FU using a crude extract and the whole cells of Ehrlich tumor cells.

The amounts of 5FdUrd formed from 5FU by a crude extract were increased in the presence of dRiblP and dUrd, although it was stimulated much more by dRiblP than by dUrd.

In the intact cells, the conversion of 5FU to 5FdUMP was also increased by dRiblP, while the presence both of dRiblP and dUrd enhanced the formation of 5FdUrd rather than that of 5FdUMP.

These results suggest that the coadministration of 5FU with dRiblP may increase the chemotherapeutic effect of 5FU.

INTRODUCTION

5-Fluorouracil (5FU) is one of the prominent antineoplastic antimetabolites. Aside from the antitumor activity of fraudulent RNA being formed from 5FU in cancer cells, its active metabolite is generally thought to be 5-fluoro-2'-deoxyuridine 5'-monophsophate (5FdUMP), which is a potent inhibitor of thymidylate synthetase[1].

Several studies have been made in order to enhance the effect of 5FU by coadministration with nucleic acid components[2,3,4]. Jato and Windheuser[2] demonstrated that 5FU coadministered with excess 2'-deoxyuridine (dUrd) had higher antitumor activity than 5FU alone against mouse leukemia L1210 and adenocarcinoma 755. Fujii et al.[3] reported that the antitumor activity of 5FU on sarcoma-180 and AH-130 tumors was enhanced by oral coadministration with uracil (Ura), although the toxicity of 5FU was also increased.

The formation of 5-fluoro-2'-deoxyuridine (5FdUrd) from 5FU and further 5FdUMP from the deoxyribonucleoside are known to be carried out according to the equations (I) and/or (II), and (III), respectively, shown in Chart 1. The present investigation deals with the formation of 5FdUrd or 5FdUMP from 5FU in the presence of 2-deoxy-α-D-ribose 1-phosphate (dRib1P) and/or dUrd by a crude extract and the intact cells of Ehrlich ascites tumor cells.

RESULTS AND DISCUSSION

1. Additive Formation of 5FdUrd from 5FU in the Presence of dRib1P and dUrd by a Crude Extract. For assay for 5FdUrd-[6-^{14}C] formed, a post-30,000 x g-centrifuged extract from homogenized tumor cells was incubated with 50 μM 5FU[6-^{14}C] in 50 mM Tris-HCl (pH 7.5) containing dRib1P and dUrd at 37° for 30 min. Aliquots of the incubation mixture were analyzed by paper chromatography (solvent: ethanol-HCl-water, 70:15:15, v/v), and then radioactivity of spots corresponding to 5FdUrd[^{14}C] and 5FU[^{14}C] was determined in a liquid scintillation spectrometer (LSS).

$$5FU + dRib1P \longrightarrow 5FdUrd \quad (I)$$
$$5FU + dUrd \longrightarrow 5FdUrd \quad (II)$$
$$5FdUrd + ATP \longrightarrow 5FdUMP \quad (III)$$

Chart 1

As shown in an example of Fig. 1, the amounts of 5FdUrd formed were increased in the various combinations of concentrations of dRib1P and dUrd to the concentrations of 5, 50, and 500 μM 5FU. In these combinations, 5 mM dRib1P exhibited an maximal effect upon the formation of 5FdUrd. Km and Vmax values for the reactions (I) and (II) involved in the formation of 5FdUrd were determined by using a crude enzyme extract.

2. Increase of Intracellular 5FdUMP in the Intact Cells When 5FU, dRib1P, and dUrd were Externally Supplied (Fig. 2). The intact cells of Ehrlich ascites tumor cells were incubated in Eagle's MEM (pH 7.2) containing 50 μM 5FU[6-^{14}C], 1 mM dRib1P, and 5 mM dUrd at 37° for 60 min. After incubation, the acid-soluble, RNA, and DNA fractions were prepared according to a Schmidt-Thannhauser-Schneider's method. Radioactivity of each of the fractions was measured in LSS. Furthermore, after the

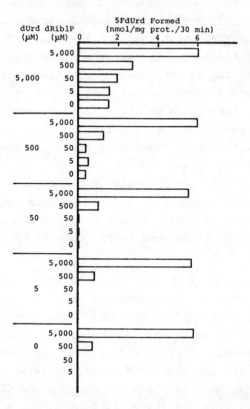

Fig. 1   Stimulating effect of dRiblP and dUrd for 5FdUrd formation from 5FU by a crude extract of Ehrlich ascites tumor cells.
5FU[14C] (5 mCi/mmol) was used at a concentration of 50 µM.

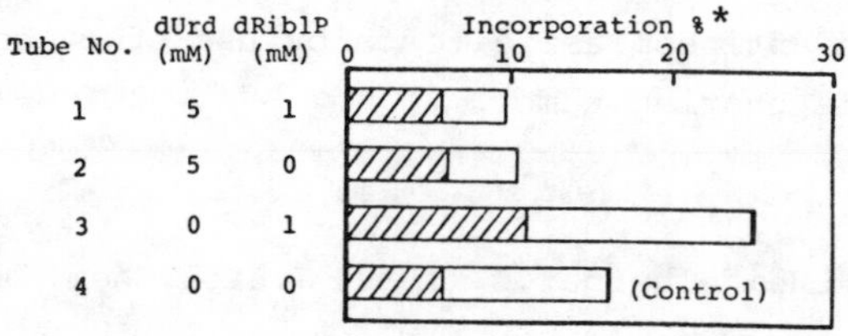

Fig. 2   Incorporation of radioactivity into acid-soluble, RNA,
and DNA fractions in intact cells which 5FU[14C] was incubated
with dRiblP and/or dUrd.
    5FU[6-14C] (10 mCi/mmol) was used at a concentration of 50 µM.
*, % of the intracellular to the applied radioactivity.

Acid-soluble RNA DNA

acid-soluble fractions were applied on Sephadex G-10 column to separate into 5FU, FU-nucleosides, and FU-nucleotides, radioactivity of each of the elutes was determined in LSS.

The uptake of radioactivity into the acid-soluble and RNA fractions was the highest in a medium containing dRiblP, and the uptake was increased to the almost same extent in the acid-soluble and RNA fractions (Tube No.3). Radioactivity of the RNA fraction was decreased by dUrd supplied in a medium even in case dUrd coexisted with dRiblP (Tube No.1 and 2). Radioactivity of DNA fraction was negligible.

By Sephadex G-10 column chromatography of the acid-soluble fractions, it was found that 5FdUrd was detected only in the fraction from cells incubated with dUrd and dRiblP, and dUrd alone, while FU-nucleotides were increased only by the supply of dRiblP.

In attempts to enhance the antitumor activity of 5FU, Windheuser and Jato[5] have already reported on the stimulating effect of dUrd in the formation from 5FU of 5FdUrd, a one-step precursor to 5FdUMP, and also on the enhancement of antitumor activity by the deoxyribonucleoside. Fujii et al. reported on a combined effect of 5FU and Ura in the antineoplastic test, and afterwards they[6] demonstrated that the degradation of 5FU in Yoshida sarcoma cells was depressed by Ura, by which the level of 5FU in the tumor tissue and the other organs was maintained higher in the Ura-treated animals than in the control animals.

We are investigating the combined effect of dRiblP for the activity of 5FU in antineoplastic tests by use of cancer cell culture and animals bearing tumor.

REFERENCES
1 Hartmann,K-U. and Heidelberger,C.(1961) J.Biol.Chem. 236,3006-3013
2 Jato,J. and Windheuser,J.J.(1973) J.Pharm.Sci. 62,1975-1978
3 Fujii,S., Ikenaka,K., Fukushima,M., and Shirasaka,T.(1978) Gann 69, 763-772
4 Kessel,D. and Hall,T.C.(1969) Cancer Res. 29,1749-1754
5 Windheuser,J.J. and Jato,J.(1972) J.Pharm.Sci. 61,1669-1670
6 Ikenaka,K., Shirasaka,T., Kitano,S., and Fujii,S.(1979) Gann 70, 353-360

Inhibition of phosphoribosylation of 5-fluorouracil by purines

Mitsuzi Yoshida, Akio Hoshi and Kazuo Kuretani

Pharmacology Division, National Cancer Center Research Institute, Tokyo 104, Japan

ABSTRACT

The mechanism of the reversal of 5-fluorouracil cytotoxicity in L5178Y cells by hypoxanthine, adenine and inosine was examined in a cell-free system. A crude extract of the cells possessed high hypoxanthine and adenine phosphoribosyltransferase and purine nucleoside phosphorylase activities. Hypoxanthine (2 mM), adenine (5 mM) and inosine (5 mM) inhibited the nucleotide formation from 5-fluorouracil at 0.2 mM 5-phosphoribosyl 1-pyrophosphate (PRPP). However, at a higher concentration of PRPP (2.5 mM), the inhibition by hypoxanthine was not found. It suggests that the inhibition of 5-fluorouracil metabolism is due to a deficiency of PRPP induced by phosphoribosylation of hypoxanthine and adenine.

INTRODUCTION

The mechanism of action of 5-fluorouracil (FU) is currently under renewed debate[1]. We have studied the mode of action of FU at the cellular level. Recently, we found complete reversal of FU cytotoxicity by hypoxanthine and adenine, whereas, it is partial by pyrimidines such as deoxyuridine and thymidine and there is no reversal by uracil, uridine or orotic acid[2]. In the present study, the mechanism of the reversal of FU cytotoxicity by purines was examined in a cell-free system.

MATERIALS AND METHODS

Reversal studies at the cellular level.   L5178Y cells were cultured in RPMI 1640 medium supplemented with 10% calf serum in a CO_2 incubator at 37°C. Cell growth was calculated by cell number after 48 hr of incubation in the presence of FU and the compound to be tested as reported previously[2].

Enzyme assay.   The supernatant fluid (100,000 x g, 60 min)

was prepared by repeated freezing and thawing of L5178Y cells suspended in 3 volumes of 50 mM Tris-HCl buffer at pH 7.4 and stored in the frozen state. Phosphoribosyltransferase activity for purines and FU was determined by the method of Schmidt et al. with modification[3]. Purine nucleoside phosphorylase activity was determined by the method of Hopkinson et al.[4]

Isoelectric focusing.   Isoelectric focusing was performed with an LKB 2117 Multiphor and Ampholine (LKB) of the pH range 3.5 to 10 according to the method of Radola with modification[5].

RESULTS AND DISCUSSION

The effect of various purines and their nucleosides on growth inhibition by FU was examined. Inosine and allopurinol reversed FU cytotoxicity, but the latter reversal was only partial because of the toxicity of allopurinol. Eleven other derivatives of purine did not show such a reversal. Hypoxanthine, adenine and the above purine derivatives may prevent the metabo-

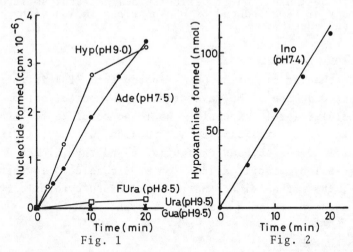

Fig. 1. Rate of phosphoribosylation of purine and pyrimidine bases by a crude extract. A mixture containing 1 mM $MgCl_2$, 2.5 mM PRPP, 0.25 M Tris-HCl or glycine buffer, a crude extract (12 mg or 1.2 mg of protein) and 3 μCi of ^{14}C-labeled substrate (specific activity: ca. 50 mCi/mmol) in a volume of 1 ml was incubated at 37°C. Formation of nucleotide was expressed as cpm per 0.1 ml reaction mixture containing 1.2 mg of protein.
Fig. 2. Enzymatic formation of hypoxanthine from inosine by a crude extract. Hypoxanthine was determined photometrically as uric acid using xanthine oxidase.

lism of FU to 5-fluorouridine monophosphate (FUMP) by inducing a
state of 5-phosphoribosyl 1-pyrophosphate (PRPP) deficiency as
we stated previously[2]. Therefore, activities of various phos-
phoribosyltransferases which utilize PRPP were examined in a
cell-free system. Phosphoribosyltransferase activities for both
hypoxanthine (H-PRT) and adenine (A-PRT) were high and that for
FU (FU-PRT) was moderate, whereas those for uracil and guanine
were negligible as shown in Fig. 1. The activity of purine nucleoside phosphorylase by which inosine was transformed into
hypoxanthine was high in a crude extract as shown in Fig. 2.

In this cell-free system, the effect of hypoxanthine, adenine and inosine on phosphoribosylation of FU was examined. At
0.2 mM PRPP, hypoxanthine (2 mM) decreased the formation of FUMP
to 50% of the control during 60 min as shown in Fig. 3, while
adenine (5 mM) and inosine (5 mM) inhibited FUMP formation weakly. This difference in the effect is considered to be due to the
difference in the optimum pH of the enzymes. At a higher concentration of PRPP (2.5 mM), hypoxanthine (2 mM) did not affect FUMP
formation (Fig. 3). These results suggest that hypoxanthine,
adenine and inosine, as a consequence of the conversion to hypoxanthine, prevent FU metabolism by a PRPP deficiency resulting
from phosphoribosylation of both purines.

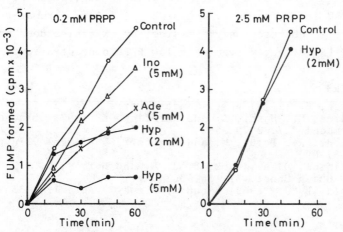

Fig. 3. Effect of hypoxanthine, adenine and inosine on phosphoribosylation of FU by a crude extract. The assay described in
Fig. 1 was used except for the addition of 2 mM dithiothreitol
and the concentration of a crude extract (0.6 mg of protein/ml).

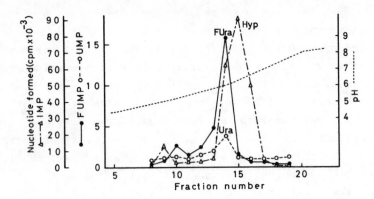

Fig. 4. Isoelectric focusing of a crude extract. A crude extract (38 mg of protein) was electrofocused in a granulated gel
(LKB, Ultrodex) containing 3.3% carrier ampholite of pH range
3.5 to 10 for 4 hr after establishing the pH gradient. Incubation times for enzyme assay were 10 min for H-PRT and 30 min
for FU-PRT and U-PRT.

To examine the reversal action in pure enzyme system, separation of H-PRT and FU-PRT was performed by isoelectric focusing
in a granulated gel. As shown in Fig. 4, H-PRT and FU-PRT had
different isoelectric points, but FU-PRT was very labile under
this treatment condition. Uracil phosphoribosyltransferase (U-
PRT) activity was also found at the site of FU-PRT. In experiments we are now conducting, preparative separation of H-PRT
and FU-PRT is performed by ion exchange column chromatography
and in this separated enzyme system, hypoxanthine does not inhibit FU-PRT directly even at a low PRPP concentration.

REFERENCES

1. Mihich, E. (1979) Bull. Cancer (Paris) 66, 37-38
2. Yoshida, M., Hoshi, A. and Kuretani, K. (1978) Biochem.
   Pharmacol. 27, 2979-2982
3. Schmidt, R., Forêt, M. and Reichert, U. (1976) Clin. Chem.
   22, 67-69
4. Hopkinson, D. A., Cook, P. J. L. and Harris, H. (1969)
   Ann. Human Genet. 32, 361-367
5. Radola, B. J. (1969) Biochim. Biophys. Acta 194, 335-338

A second site specific endonuclease from Thermus thermophilus 111, Tth111II

Takahisa Shinomiya, Mariko Kobayashi and Showbu Sato

Mitsubishi-Kasei Institute of Life Sciences, Minamiooya 11, Machida, Tokyo 194, Japan

ABSTRACT

A second site specific endonuclease with a novel specificity has been isolated from <u>Thermus thermophilus</u> strain 111 and named <u>Tth111II</u>. The enzyme is active at temperature up to 80°C and requires Mg^{2+} or Mn^{2+} for activity. <u>Tth111II</u> cleaves ϕX174RFDNA into 11 fragments. From the analysis of 5' terminal sequences of the ϕX174RFDNA fragments produced by <u>Tth111II</u> action, it was concluded that Tth111II recognized the DNA sequence 5' CAAPuCA(N)$_{11}$ $\downarrow$3'
3' GTTPyGT(N)$_9$ $\uparrow$5'
and cleaved the sites as indicated by arrows.

INTRODUCTION

A number of site specific endonuleases (type II restriction endonucleases) which were indispensable for dissection of genomes and for DNA sequencing [1] have been purified from various microorganisms [2].

In extreme thermophilic bacteria, we have sought thermostable restriction endonucleases with novel specificity, which would aid studies on the mechanisms of the action of restriction endonucleases as well as studies of DNA structure. Recently, we have reported site specific endonucleases in <u>T. thermophilus</u> strain HB8 [3] and 111 [4]. They are named <u>TthHB8I</u> and <u>Tth111I</u>. The former is an isoschizomer of <u>TaqI</u> and the later is an enzyme with a novel specificity (5'GACNNNGTC 3').

We have found in <u>T. thermophilus</u> 111 another site specific endonuclease, <u>Tth111II</u> which has a unique specificity. This paper describes the purification of <u>Tth111II</u> and its recognition sequence.

EXPERIMENTAL RESULTS AND CONCLUSION

<u>Isolation of Tth111II</u>: Frozen cells (850 g) of <u>T. thermophilus</u> 111 (harvested at a stationary phase using jar fermentor) were thawed in 1700 ml of 20 mM Tris-HCl (pH8.0) / 1 mM EDTA / 5 mM 2-mercaptoethanol / 0.15 M NaCl and disrupted by sonication. After centrifugation at 30,000 g for 3 h, the

supernatant was applied to a DEAE-cellulose column. Non-adsorbed fractions
containing Tth111II were pooled and applied on to a column of phospho-
cellulose. The column was developed with a
NaCl gradient (0.15 - 1.0 M in 10 mM potassium
phosphate, pH7.4). Tth111II was eluted in
fractions of 0.4 - 0.6 M NaCl. The active
fractions were pooled, diluted with 3 volumes
of water and adsorbed on to a column of
Heparin-Sepharose4B. The elution was carried
out with a linear gradient of NaCl (0.15 - 0.8
M). Tth111II was eluted arround 0.6 M NaCl.
The active fractions were pooled, diluted again
with 5 volumes of water and adsorbed on to a
column of hydroxylapatite. The elution was
performed with a linear gradient of potassium
phosphate (pH7.4) from 0.001 to 1.0 M under
0.1 M NaCl concentration. Tth111II eluted in
fractions of 0.03 - 0.1 M potassium phosphate.
These fractions were used in subsequent
experiments.

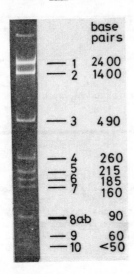

	base pairs
— 1	2400
— 2	1400
— 3	490
— 4	260
— 5	215
— 6	185
— 7	160
— 8ab	90
— 9	60
— 10	<50

Fig.1. Gel electrophoresis
of Tth111II digest of
øX174RFDNA

Cleavage sites of Tth111II on øX174RFDNA: When the digest of øX174RFDNA
with Tth111II was analysed on 5 % polyacrylamide slab gel (Fig.1), eleven
bands (designated 1 to 10 from large to small) appeared with stain of ethidium bromide. Sizes of the fragments were estimated by means of the plot of
electrophoretic mobility vs. molecular sizes of known restriction fragments.
In order to determine Tth111II cleavage sites on øX174RFDNA, double digestion
with Tth111II and HinfI, TthHB8I, HaeIII or HindII was carried out. Taking
into account of the sizes of the Tth111II fragments and results of the double
digestions, we have roughly estimated the positions of Tth111II cleavage
sites as illustrated in Fig.2.

Two dimensional mapping of 5' terminal sequence of Tth111II cleavage
site: øX174RFDNA was digested with Tth111II and electrophoresed on 5 % polyacrylamide slab gel. Each DNA band was cut out and electrophoretically
eluted from the gel into a dialysis bag. The eluted fragment was collected
with an ethanol precipitation. The different three fragments corresponding
to the band 3, 4 and 5 in Fig.1 were treated with alkaline phosphatase, and
labeled at the 5' ends using polynucleotide kinase with $[\gamma-^{32}P]$ATP. Each
fragment was digested with another appropriate restriction endonuclease

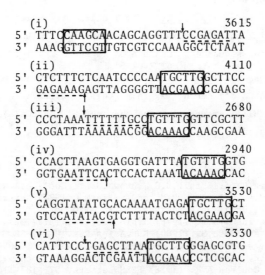

Fig.2. Cleavage map of φX174RFDNA. The positions of Tth111II cleavage sites determined in this paper are shown in relation to the known restriction fragment maps of other enzymes [2].

```
       (i)                        ↓        3615
5' TTTC CAAGCA ACAGCAGGTTTCC GAGATTA
3' AAAG GTTCGT TGTCGTCCAAAGGCTCTAAT

       (ii)                              4110
5' CTCTTTCTCAATCCCCAA TGCTTG GCTTCC
3' GAGAAAGAGTTAGGGGTT ACGAAC CGAAGG

       (iii)    ↓                        2680
5' CCCTAAATTTTTTGCC TGTTTG GTTCGCTT
3' GGGATTTAAAAAAACGG ACAAAC CAAGCGAA

       (iv)                              2940
5' CCACTTAAGTGAGGTGATTTA TGTTTG GTG
3' GGTGAATTCACTCCACTAAAT ACAAAC CAC

       (v)                               3530
5' CAGGTATATGCACAAAATGAGA TGCTTG CT
3' GTCCATATACGTCTTTTACTCT ACGAAC GA

       (vi)     ↓                        3330
5' CATTTCC TGAGCTTAA TGCTTG GGAGCGTG
3' GTAAAGGACTCGAATT ACGAAC CCTCGCAC
```

Fig.3. Sequences around six Tth111II cleavage sites are shown by arrows, and the common sequences are boxed. The sequences determined by the two dimensional homochromatography are indicated by broken underlining. The sequences were established in the following Tth111II fragments double digested with other restriction endonucleases; (i) and (ii), Tth111II number 3 fragment / HindII digests; (iii) and (iv), Tth111II number 4 fragment / HpaII digests; (v) and (vi), Tth111II number 5 fragment / HindII digests. The sequences are presented with the viral DNA sequence in the upper line. The numbers refer to the distance of the 3' end of the viral DNA sequences from the PstI site [2,7].

(e.g. HindII for number 3 and 5 fragment; HpaII for number 4 fragment) and
DNA fragments ^{32}P-labeled at one 5' end were separated by gel electrophoresis. Each DNA fragment in which only 5' end produced by Tth111II action had
been ^{32}P-labeled was partially digested with pancreatic DNase. One-fifth of
the above digest was treated with venom phosphodiesterase to liberate
labeled mononucleotides. The mixture of digestion products was fractionated
by the two dimensional homochromatography. The two dimensional homochromatography developed by Brownlee and Sanger [5] was used with some modification
described by Tu et al. [6]. The experimental results were arranged for the
help of understanding and shown in Fig.3. The sequences, 5' CAAGCA 3' and
5' CAAACA 3', are observed at a distance of 11 bases apart from cleavage
points (Fig.3. i, ii, iv and v). Their complementary sequences, 5' GTTTGT 3'
and 5' GTTCGT 3', are observed as well at a distance of 9 bases apart from
cleavage points (Fig.3. iii and vi). These results suggest that Tth111II
should have a recognition sequences as 5' CAAPuCA(N)$_{11}$$\downarrow$ 3' and cleave at the
sites indicated by arrows. 3' GTTPyGT(N)$_{9}$↑ 5'

   Localization of Tth111II site: The Tth111II recognition sites were
tested by searching on φX174RFDNA sequence reported by Sanger et al. [2,7].
The location of the sequence 5' CAAPuCA 3' is shown in Fig.2 and fairly
                          3' GTTPyGT 5'
matched for the observed Tth111II cleavage sites. Another sequence except
this (e.g. 5' CAANCA 3') can not explain Tth111II sites. Therefor, we have
concluded that Tth111II recognizes the sequence 5' CAAPuCA(N)$_{11}$$\downarrow$ 3' and
                                                3' GTTPyGT(N)$_{9}$↑ 5'
cleaves as indicated by arrows.

REFERENCES
1. Sanger,F., Air,G.M., Barell,B.G., Brown,N.L., Coulson,A.R., Fiddes,J.C.,
    HutchsonIII,C.A., Slocombe,P.M. and Smith,M. (1977) Nature 265, 687-695
2. Roberts,R.J. (1980) Nuc Acids Res. 8, r63-r80
3. Sato,S. and Shinomiya,T. (1978) J.Biochem. 84, 1319-1321
4. Shinomiya,T. and Sato,S. (1980) Nuc.Acids Res. 8, 43-56
5. Brownlee,G.G. and Sanger,F. (1969) Eur.J.Biochem. 11, 395-399
6. Tu,C.D., Jay,E., Bahl,C.P. and Wu,R. (1976) Anal.Biochem. 74, 73-
7. Sanger,F. and Coulson,A.R. (1978) FEBS Letters, 87, 107-110

Inhibition of terminal deoxynucleotidyltransferase by various diadenosine polyphosphates

Katsuhiko Ono*, Yukari Iwata*, Hiromu Nakamura** and Akio Matsukage[+]

Laboratories of Viral Oncology*, Experimental Radiology** and Biochemistry[+], Aichi Cancer Center Research Institute, Chikusa-ku, Nagoya 464, Japan

ABSTRACT

Terminal deoxynucleotidyltransferase (TdT) was found to be strongly inhibited by diadenosine $5',5'''-P^1,P^4$-tetraphosphate (Ap_4A) while other mammalian DNA polymerases α, β and γ were neither inhibited nor activated by Ap_4A. Such inhibitory effect on TdT was also observed with a variety of diadenosine polyphosphates (Ap_nA), n=3-6) when TdT activity was assayed by determining incorporation of dCTP. Kinetic analysis revealed that the inhibition of TdT by Ap_nA was due to competition with substrate deoxynucleoside triphosphate(s).

INTRODUCTION

In the studies of backreaction of amino acid activation in protein synthesizing system, Zamecnik et al. found a new adenine nucleotide and identified it as diadenosine $5'$, $5'''-P^1$, P^4-tetraphosphate ($A_{p_4}A$) (1,2). Later, this $A_{p_4}A$ was suggested to act as a signal molecule (3) for mammalian cell growth, since intracellular concentration of this compound fluctuates in proportion to the proliferation rate of the cells (4). Recently, Grummt demonstrated that addition of $A_{p_4}A$ to permeabilized G_1-arrested BHK cells initiated DNA synthesis (5). Furthermore, it was shown that $A_{p_4}A$ specifically binds to Mr 57,000 polypeptide of calf thymus DNA polymerase α (6). The result suggests that DNA polymerase α is a intracellular target of $A_{p_4}A$. However, effect of $A_{p_4}A$ on the activity of DNA polymerase α has not been examined.

In this paper, we describe that $A_{p_4}A$ has no remarkable effect on the activities of purified DNA polymerases α, β and γ from mouse myeloma and that this compound inhibits the activity of terminal deoxynucleotidyltransferase (TdT) from calf thymus.

Furthermore, inhibitory effects of a series of diadenosine polyphosphates are described.

MATERIALS AND METHODS

Chemicals. [^{3}H]dNTP's were purchased from Radiochemical Centre, Amersham, England. Unlabeled dNTP's were obtained from Boehringer Mannheim, West Germany. $A_{Pn}A$ and $(dA)_{12-18}$ were the products of P-L Biochemicals, Inc., Milwaukee, Wis. Calf thymus DNA from Sigma Chemical Co., St. Louis, Mo., was activated according to the method of Schlabach et al. (7). DEAE-cellulose paper (DE81, $\phi23$ mm) was from Whatman Ltd., Springfield Mill, Maidstone, Kent, England.

DNA polymerases α, β and γ and TdT. DNA polymerases α (8), β (9) and γ (10) were purified from mouse myeloma MOPC104E cells as described previously. TdT was purified from calf thymus to homogeneity as described elsewhere (11).

Assays for DNA polymerases and TdT. The activity of DNA polymerases α, β and γ was assayed with activated calf thymus DNA as described elsewhere (12). The assay mixture (50 μl) for TdT contained the followings; 0.1 M Hepes (pH 8.0), 6 μg/ml $(dA)_{12-18}$, 0.5 mM $MnCl_2$, 30 mM KCl, 1 mM DTT, 15% (v/v) glycerol, 400 μg/ml bovine serum albumin and 10 μM [^{3}H]dCTP. All reactions were carried out at 37°C for 30 min, stopped by adding 15 μl of 0.2 M EDTA and the product DNA on DE81 filter paper was assayed as previously described (13).

RESULTS AND DISCUSSION

Effect of $A_{P4}A$ on the activities of DNA polymerases α, β and γ and TdT. Fig. 1 shows the effect of $A_{P4}A$ on the activities of mouse myeloma DNA polymerases α, β and γ and calf thymus TdT. $A_{P4}A$ had no remarkable effect on DNA polymerases α, β and γ, whereas TdT was strongly inhibited by low concentrations of $A_{P4}A$. Furthermore, other $A_{Pn}A$'s such as $A_{P3}A$, $A_{P5}A$ and $A_{P6}A$ exhibited similar extent of inhibition of TdT (data not shown). Thus, TdT is sensitive to a wide range of the number of phosphate groups in $A_{Pn}A$'s (n=3-6). This property of TdT is distinct from that of DNA polymerase α the binding activity of which is highly specific for $A_{P4}A$ (6), and also different from that of rabbit muscle

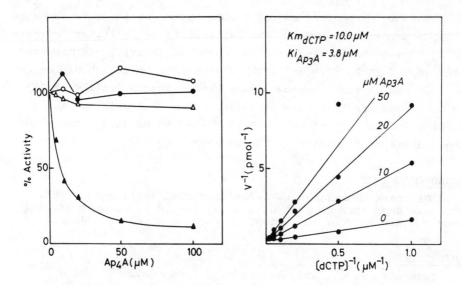

Fig. 1 (left). Effect of $A_{P4}A$ on the activities of DNA polymerases α, β and γ and TdT. Assay conditions were as described in the text. Concentrations of $A_{P4}A$ are indicated in the figure. Concentrations of [³H]dTTP were constant at 10 μM (600 cpm/pmol) for DNA polymerases α (●) and β ($\triangle$) and at 1 μM (6,000 cpm/pmol) for DNA polymerase γ (○). Concentrations of [³H]dCTP (200 cpm/pmol) were constant at 10 μM for TdT (▲). 100% activities (pmoles) correspond to 24.8 (●), 2.4 ($\triangle$), 11.5 (○) and 42.9 (▲).

Fig. 2 (right). Analysis of inhibition of TdT by $A_{P3}A$. Reactions were carried out under the assay conditions described in the text, except that various concentrations of [³H]dCTP (180 cpm/pmol) were used in the presence of 0, 10, 20 and 50 μM $A_{P3}A$. The figure represents double reciprocal plot.

adenylate kinase to which only $A_{P5}A$ is very inhibitory (14).

Mode of inhibition of TdT by $A_{Pn}A$ and kinetic constants. The mode of inhibition of TdT by $A_{Pn}A$ was in all cases competitive to the substrate dNTP. A typical example with $A_{P3}A$ is shown in Fig. 2. On the contrary, the inhibition of TdT by $A_{Pn}A$ was noncompetitive with respect to the primer (dA)$_{12-18}$ (data not shown). These results indicate that the binding site for dNTP is different from that for primer. Ki values of TdT for $A_{Pn}A$'s were estimated to be 3.8, 3.0, 1.9 and 1.7 for $A_{P3}A$, $A_{P4}A$, $A_{P5}A$ and $A_{P6}A$, respectively. These values were lower than Km value for dCTP (10.0 μM). The result that inhibitory effect of $A_{Pn}A$ on TdT increases by increasing the number of the phosphate groups of the compound indicates that phosphate moiety is important for the inhibitory action.

TdT can polymerize any of the 4 deoxynucleoside triphosphates at 3'-OH end of the primer. Similar results of inhibitory effects of $A_{pn}A$ on TdT were also obtained when TdT activity was measured with any of dATP, dGTP and dTTP as substrate. Although biological role of TdT is still unknown, such strong susceptibility of TdT to $A_{pn}A$ suggests that some peculiar control mechanism(s) is working for TdT in the cell. $A_{pn}A$'s seem to be useful tools for the studies of mechanism of DNA synthesis by TdT.

ACKNOWLEDGMENTS

We thank Miss I. Inagaki for technical assistance. This work was supported in part by a Grant-in-Aid for Cancer Research from the Ministry of Education, Science, and Culture, Japan.

REFERENCES

1 Zamecnik, P. C., Stephenson, M. L., Janeway, C. M. and Randerath, K. (1966) Biochem. Biophys. Res. Commun. 24, 91-97
2 Randerath, K., Janeway, C. M., Stephenson, M. L. and Zamecnik, P. C. (1966) Biochem. Biophys. Res. Commun. 24, 98-105
3 Tomkins, G. M. (1975) Science 189, 760-763
4 Rapaport, E. and Zamecnik, P. C. (1976) Proc. Natl. Acad Sci. USA 73, 3984-3988
5 Grummt, F. (1978) Proc. Natl. Acad. Sci. USA 75, 371-375
6 Grummt, F., Waltl, G., Jantzen, H.-M., Hamprecht, K., Huebscher, U. and Kuenzle, C. C. (1979) Proc. Natl. Acad Sci. USA 76, 6081-6085
7 Schlabach, A., Friedlender, B., Bolden, A. and Weissbach, A. (1971) Biochem. Biophys. Res. Commun. 44, 879-885
8 Matsukage, A., Sivarajan, M. and Wilson, S. H. (1976) Biochemistry 15, 5305-5314
9 Ono, K., Ohashi, A., Tanabe, K., Matsukage, A., Nishizawa, M. and Takahashi, T. (1979) Nucleic Acids Res. 7, 715-726
10 Matsukage, A., Bohn, E. W. and Wilson, S. H. (1975) 14, 1006-1020
11 Nakamura, H., Morita, T. and Yoshida, S., submitted for publication
12 Ono, K., Ohashi, A., Yamamoto, A., Matsukage, A., Takahashi, T., Saneyoshi, M. and Ueda, T. (1979) Cancer Res. 39, 4673-4680
13 Lindell, T. J., Weinberg, F., Morris, P. W., Roeder, R. G. and Rutter, W. J. (1967) Science 170, 447-449
14 Lienhard, G. E. and Secemski, I. I. (1973) J. Biol. Chem. 248, 1121-1123

Utilization of 5-alkyl UTPs by DNA-dependent RNA polymerase I and II purified from cherry salmon (Onchorhynchus masou) liver

Chikao Nakayama and Mineo Saneyoshi

Faculty of Pharmaceutical Sciences, Hokkaido University, Sapporo 060, Japan

Abstract

DNA dependent RNA polymerase II was purified to approximately 8300 fold from sonicated nuclear extract of cherry salmon (*Onchorhynchus masou*) liver by the following purification steps: polyethylene glycol treatment, DEAE-Sephadex A-25 column chromatography, heparin-Sepharose column chromatography, and affinity chromatography on DNA-cellulose. Final preparation of this enzyme has a specific activity of 157 nmole UMP incorporation into RNA per mg of protein per 10 min at 25°. RNA polymerase I was also purified to approx. 3800 fold in a similar manner. Its specific activity was calculated as 26.2 nmole/mg/10 min. Utilization of various UTPs of these enzymes was studied by substitution experiments under the condition of limited synthesis. 5-Methyl UTP (rTTP) could be utilized by the RNA polymerase I 1.7 fold more efficiently compared with UTP. In contrast, the RNA polymerase II recognized rTTP as a substrate as efficiently as UTP. Similar experiments using other alkyl UTPs have been performed.

Introduction

Utilization of a number of nucleotide analogues as substrates or inhibitors in polymerization of rNTPs in RNA polymerase system of *E. coli* has been extensively studied.[1,2] On the other hand, very little is known in eukaryotic system, except that cordycepin 5'-triphosphate has been studied in several eukaryotic RNA polymerase systems as an inhibitor.[3,4]

In order to obtain some basic knowledge in developing selective enzyme inhibitors in eukaryotic RNA polymerase systems, we have tried to establish a purification method of the polymerases from cherry salmon (*Onchorhynchus masou*) liver and studied the interaction between the RNA polymerases and certain 5-alkyl UTPs.

Materials and Methods

Liver of cherry salmon was collected at Mori branch, Hokkaido Fish Hatchery and immediately frozen by solid carbon dioxide and stored at -80° until use.

UTP analogues were synthesized from corresponding nucleosides[5] by phosphory-

lation with phosphorus oxychloride[6] followed by further derivatization to
5'-triphosphate by using phosphoromorpholidate method.[7]

Purification of RNA polymerase I and II from cherry salmon liver

Purification steps are summarized in Table I.

Table I Step	Volume (ml)	Total protein (mg)	Activity (units)[+]	Specific activity (units/mg)	Fold
Nuclear extract[++]	71	1832	12.6 (I) 35.3 (II)	0.007 0.019	1
RNA polymerase I					
DEAE-Sephadex	30	7.74	4.6	0.59	86
Heparin-Sepharose	4.2	0.21	5.5	26.2	3800
RNA polymerase II					
DEAE-Sephadex	49	6.52	31.4	4.8	250
Heparin-Sepharose	2.9	0.5	23.9	47.8	2520
DNA-cellulose	1.0	0.18	28.3	157.2	8270

+ One unit = 1 nmole of UMP incorporated to RNA in 10 min at 25°.
++ Starting from 250 g of frozen salmon liver.

Assay conditions of RNA polymerase activity

Assay conditions of RNA polymerase activity were employed according to
Roeder[8] with a slight modification as follows. The standard incubation
mixture contained in 50 µl: 50 mM Tris-HCl pH 7.9, 1 mM $MnCl_2$, 0.1 mM EDTA,
4 mM DTT, 10 µg of native salmon sperm DNA, 20% glycerol, 25 µg of BSA,
500 µM ATP, CTP, GTP, 10 µM UTP and 1 µCi of ^{3}H-UTP. Ammonium sulfate
concentration in the mixture was 60 mM and 110 mM for RNA polymerase I and
II, respectively. After incubation at 25° for 10 min, the reaction was
terminated by pipetting onto DEAE-cellulose disk. After washing with 5% sodium
phosphate, radioactivity remaining on the filter was counted.

Assay conditions in substitution experiments

The incubation mixture was the same as that of standard assay condition
of RNA polymerase activity except that 50 µM each of ATP, CTP and 10 µM of GTP
and 1-2 µCi of ^{3}H-GTP were used as the limited synthesis. Addition of UTP
analogues in this mixture caused stimulation of the incorporation of ^{3}H-GMP
into RNA.
Comparison of the complete system (presence of UTP), with the above system,
showed effectiveness of the UTP analogues as a substrate.

Results

Effect of UTP analogues on the incorporation of ^{3}H-GMP into RNA is shown in Fig 1. As can be seen in Fig 1, differential effect of rTTP on RNA polymerase I and II is apparent.

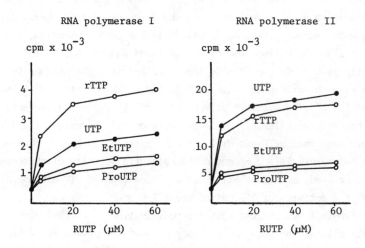

Fig 1. Stimulation of ^{3}H-GMP incorporation into RNA by the addition of UTP analogues under the condition of limited synthesis.

In order to clarify the differential response between RNA polymerase I and II to 5-alkyl UTPs, kinetic parameters of each enzyme have been determined. The results are summarized in Table II.

Table II. Kinetic parameters of various substrates on RNA synthesis catalyzed by RNA polymerases.

Compound	RNA polymerase I		RNA polymerase II	
	Km (μM)	V_{max}^{rel}	Km (μM)	V_{max}^{rel}
UTP	7	1.00	3	1.00
rTTP	5	1.67	4	1.07
EtUTP	10	0.63	9	0.32
ProUTP	17	0.55	11	0.29

Discussion

The substrate specificity of DNA-dependent RNA polymerases from vertebrates has not been reported so far. This paper is to be the first report on the utilization of UTP analogues as substrates in RNA polymerase system in eukaryotes as well as vertebrates. We have studied the ability of 5-alkyl UTPs as substrates in both RNA polymerase I and II purified from cherry salmon (*Onchorhynchus masou*) liver. As described in the results section, it has been found that rTTP can be replaced by UTP in these RNA polymerase system as efficiently as UTP. In contrast to the above results, RNA polymerase of *E. coli* has a Km value of rTTP which was six fold larger than that of UTP^2. We found that Km value of rTTP with RNA polymerase I and II was not different. The Vmax values, however, were largely different between RNA polymerase I and II. This would mean that rTTP was utilized more efficiently by RNA polymerase I than RNA polymerase II and enhanced the catalytic activity of the enzyme. On the other hand, methyl substitution at 5-position of UTP did not affect the catalytic activity of RNA polymerase II.

These findings may suggest that the modification of 5-alkyl UTPs, especially rTTP at the sugar portion may be useful approach for designing new selective inhibitors either RNA polymerase I or II.

Acknowledgement

The authors are indebted to Mr. M. Uchiyama, Director of Mori Branch, Hokkaido Fish Hatchery and his staffs for collecting cherry salmon liver in September, 1978 and 1979.

References

1) Kahan, F.M. and Hurwitz, J., (1962), *J. Biol. Chem.*, 237, 3778-3785

2) Slapikoff, S. and Berg, P. (1967), *Biochemistry*, 6, 3654-3658

3) Blatti, S.P., Ingles, C.J., Morris, P.W., Weave, R.F., Weinberg, F. and Rutter, W.J., (1970) *Cold Spring Harbor Sym. Quant. Biol.*, 35, 649-659

4) Horwitz, B., Goldfinger, B.A. and Murmur (1976) *Arch. Biochem. Biophys.*, 172, 143-148

5) Nakayama, C., Machida, H. and Saneyoshi, M. (1979) *J. Carbohydr. Nucleosides and Nucleotides*, 6, 295-308

6) Yoshikawa, M., Kato, T. and Takenishi, T. (1967) *Tetrahedron Lett.*, 5065-5068

7) Moffatt, J.G. (1964) *Can. J. Biochem.*, 42, 599

8) Roeder, R.G. (1974) *J. Biol. Chem.*, 249, 241-248